This volume covers foundations from the architect's point of view. The principles which must be applied to ensure, without great cost, safe and lasting foundations are fully described. The penalties for not meeting these essential requirements are great.

In considering the properties of the foundation soil, the architect must remember that these properties depend upon the type of building erected on the soil and that the properties vary with time. In the first two parts of the book—*Soil and Water* and *Loadings and Tests*—the reader is introduced to the fundamentals of the subject. No advanced mathematics is used. In part three—*Designing for Stability*—the problems of bearing capacity and settlement are fully considered.

The book is written in such a way that the older practising architect who wishes merely to survey the general field of existing knowledge of foundations can do so. Simultaneously, the younger graduate or practising architect who wishes to go into precise detail can take their studies further by working through the computation panels. There, the effects of water, the influence of varying soils and the relationship between soil and structure are developed.

The architect must increasingly rely on scientific appraisal of data presented to him. The factors influencing his problems have made books of this kind both necessary and welcome. The architectural profession is producing trained men and women who are able not only to apply general architectural knowledge, but also skills directed to more specialised aspects of their professional work. Together with other books in the Architectural Science Series, this work will considerably facilitate development and application of an analytical and soundly based approach to architectural practice in a form which will become increasingly important in coming decades.

The book is of particular interest to architectural students and to practising architects, but workers in fields ancillary to the building industry will find it of special interest and value.

Fundamental Foundations

ELSEVIER ARCHITECTURAL SCIENCE SERIES

Editor

HENRY J. COWAN

Professor of Architectural Science
University of Sydney

Previously published

An Historical Outline of Architectural Science
by H. J. COWAN

Thermal Performance of Buildings
by J. F. VAN STRAATEN

Computers in Architectural Design
by D. CAMPION

In Press

Models in Architecture
by H. J. COWAN, G. D. DING, J. S. GERO AND R. W. MUNCEY

Projected titles

Architecture and Climate
Designing for Health and Comfort
Solar Control of Buildings
Principles of Air Conditioning
Vertical Transportation — Elevator and Escalator Systems
for Multi-storey Buildings
Electrical Services in Buildings
Principles of Illumination and Natural Lighting
Artificial Lighting of Buildings
Architectural Acoustics
Control of Fire in Buildings
Evaluation of Building Materials
The Choice of Structure
The Design of Building Frames
Shells and Space Frames
Analytical Techniques of Planning
Architecture and Systems Analysis

Fundamental Foundations

by

W. FISHER CASSIE, C.B.E.

Professor of Civil Engineering
University of Newcastle upon Tyne

Fellow of the Royal Society of Edinburgh
Past President: Institution of Highway Engineers
Member: Institution of Civil Engineers
Member: Institution of Structural Engineers

ELSEVIER PUBLISHING COMPANY

AMSTERDAM – LONDON – NEW YORK

1968

ELSEVIER PUBLISHING COMPANY LIMITED
BARKING, ESSEX, ENGLAND

ELSEVIER PUBLISHING COMPANY
335 JAN VAN GALENSTRAAT, P.O. BOX 211, AMSTERDAM,
THE NETHERLANDS

AMERICAN ELSEVIER PUBLISHING COMPANY INC.
52 VANDERBILT AVENUE, NEW YORK N.Y. 10017

LIBRARY OF CONGRESS CATALOG CARD NUMBER 68–17575

WITH 72 ILLUSTRATIONS AND 41 TABLES

Printed in Great Britain by Galliard Limited, Great Yarmouth, England

Conversion to Metric System of the Units Used

The modern metric system is the *Système International d'Unités*, commonly known as the SI system. The older metric system, still in use but being superseded by the SI system, is known as the *metric technical system*. The chief difference between the two is in the definition of force or load.

Throughout this book the terms ton, lb and kg are used to indicate the load produced when the acceleration due to gravity acts on a mass of one ton, lb or kg, respectively. These loads should, more correctly, be described as tonf, lbf and kgf to distinguish them as forces from the similar ton, lb and kg, which are, strictly, masses. In architecture, however, most forces are caused by the action of gravity and the shorter term is understood. Wind loads form a separate category.

In the SI system, the unit of force is considered detached from the influence of gravity, and is represented by the force which is necessary to give a unit acceleration to a unit mass (one kg accelerated to one metre per second, in each second). This new unit of force is one NEWTON (symbol N, or kN for 1000 newtons).

The conversions below cover most of the figures used in this book and give both SI and metric technical units. Conversions are given to four significant figures.

Length
 ft multiplied by 0·3048 gives m
 in multiplied by 2·540 gives cm

Cross-sectional area
 ft^2 multiplied by 929·0 gives cm^2
 in^2 multiplied by 6·452 gives cm^2

Volume

    ft^3 multiplied by 0·02832 gives m^3
    in^3 multiplied by 16·39   gives cm^3 (ml)

Mass and force, or load

    ton multiplied by 1016   gives kg
    ton multiplied by 9964   gives N
    lb multiplied by 453·6   gives g
    lb multiplied by   4·448 gives N

Line load

    ton/ft multiplied by 3333   gives kg/m
    ton/ft multiplied by 32·69 gives kN/m
    lb/in multiplied by 0·1786 gives kg/cm
    lb/in multiplied by 1·751 gives N/cm

Pressure

    ton/ft^2 multiplied by 107·3   gives kN/m^2
    ton/in^2 multiplied by 157·5   gives kg/cm^2
    lb/ft^2 multiplied by 4·883   gives kg/m^2
    lb/ft^2 multiplied by 47·88   gives N/m^2
    lb/in^2 multiplied by 7·030   gives kg/mm^2
    lb/in^2 multiplied by 6·895   gives kN/m^2
    ton/ft^2 multiplied by $10·94 \times 10^3$ gives kg/m^2

Density: seepage force

    lb/ft^3 multiplied by   0·01602 gives g/cm^3 (g/ml)
    lb/ft^3 multiplied by 157·1   gives N/m^3

Rate of flow

    ft^3/sec (cusec) multiplied by 0·02832 gives m^3/sec

Coefficient of permeability: velocity of flow

    ft/year multiplied by 57·96 $\times 10^6$ gives cm/min
    ft/day multiplied by 0·9659 $\times 10^6$ gives cm/sec
    in/min multiplied by 4·233 $\times 10^6$ gives micron/sec
       (One micron is one μm or one-millionth of a metre.)

Coefficient of compressibility

in^2/lb multiplied by 1422   gives mm^2/kg

ft^2/ton multiplied by   0·9144 gives cm^2/kg

Coefficient of consolidation

ft^2/day multiplied by   0·003871 gives m^2/h

ft^2/h multiplied by 814·3   gives $m^2/year$

in^2/min multiplied by 387·1   gives cm^2/h

(in^2/min equals $10ft^2/day$.)

Contents

PART I

SOIL AND WATER

The Problems Posed
Properties of Soils
Above and Below the Water Table

Chapter 1

The Problems Posed

1.1. Soil Mechanics in Architectural Practice

This book is concerned only with that aspect of soil mechanics which is of particular interest to architects—building foundations—and the treatment of the subject matter is directed to the architectural student and to the young architect in practice. He is helped, by text and by sample computations, to understand the complex inter-relation of soils and foundation substructures. He should gradually realise, as he works through the book, how the behaviour of the soil on which the building is founded is closely dependent on the design of both the substructure and the superstructure of the building.

Throughout the centuries, until recently, the architect had only his own experience and that of his fellow workers to guide him in the design of foundations. He thought of the foundation soil (if he thought of it at all during the preliminary designs) as having a certain "strength" which would support the weight of his building. His approach to the design of foundations was, and often still is, intuitive and subjective.

Intuitive design, based on knowledge, flair, experience and professional ability, must continue. Nothing can replace it entirely. It is of the essence of creative architectural thought. This must be emphasised, for it is sometimes assumed that the calculations which form part of the subject of soil mechanics entirely replace design of the old type. This is not so; such a substitution could never take place with safety to the building.

Engineers have applied the techniques of physics, mathematics and engineering to the study of foundations, but it cannot be claimed that, by these techniques alone, the inexperienced architect can acquire all the knowledge necessary for the invariably successful design of foundations. The studies in this volume are intended as supports and guides to the well-established methods. They depict, briefly, the simpler aspects of the knowledge which has gradually

3

accumulated since scientific study was directed towards foundations of buildings. This knowledge strengthens the architect's confidence in his sub-surface designs. Several decades have elapsed since the late Dr. Karl Terzaghi, the "father" of soil mechanics, addressed the American Society of Civil Engineers on *The Science of Foundations —its Present and Future*. This paper, an outstanding piece of creative thinking, gave a stimulus to research and marked a change in direction of thought and an expansion of knowledge.

1.2. Need for Studies of Soils in Foundations

The need for the application by architects themselves (and not merely by their specialist consultants) of the collected knowledge of the behaviour of foundations stems from the greater mobility of the practitioner and the greater range of experiment in structural styles evident today. Experience alone is a good guide only if the conditions of the new problems approximate to those of the old. Today, with the increasing concentration of populations in urban centres, sites are being used which would have been avoided in times past as presenting too many difficulties. The need to use sites where conditions are poor, or sites encumbered with the remains of former foundations, will increase as the years pass.

Formerly, the pupil learned from his master and became wise about the sites of his region by constant familiarity with their narrow range of problems. This comfortable background of local and personal knowledge, and of confidence in locally developed designs, is lost as practitioners work far from their home base in regions the soils of which are unknown to them. If, in addition, a projected building offers a new approach to structural interpretation, or is merely very much larger than the architect's normal designs, caution is required. Intuitive design of foundations must then be supported by scientifically based knowledge or, as has been shown so many times, there may be unfortunate consequences.

1.3. Interdependence of Soil and Building

The architect reading this book must first unburden himself of the conventional idea that the building "stands" on the ground which has a definite and fixed property known as the "bearing capacity". The first stage in the scientific study of foundations must be a reorientation of the architect's process of thought. In his mind's eye he should visualise his building as being stressed between two sets of forces. Those applied from above by the various natural and artificial loadings must be balanced by those applied from below by the soil of the site. Once the resistance required from the soil by the presence of the building has been evaluated, its value must be consistent with the ability of the soil to develop the forces needed. If the design of the building—both substructure and superstructure—is not matched to the ability of the soil to provide the forces of resistance, functional failure will ensue. The study of the soil must not only be made at an early stage before the design of the building has gone further than the sketch form, but soil study must form an integral part of the preliminary design of the building.

In considering the properties of the foundation soil, the architect must also remember that these properties are not only dependent on the type of building erected on the soil, but that they also vary with time. Long after the building is completed the extra load it applies continues to change the properties of the soil, so that it, eventually, becomes a different material. As time passes the soil reacts by changes in form and properties. These changes must be predicted and taken into account in the early stages of design. No soil can ever be accepted as a static unchanging material with constant properties.

From the viewpoint of the enlightened architect, therefore, the building is not a structural creation in its own right, passively standing on the soil. It is a part of a greater complex, of which the mass of soil stressed by the presence of the building forms as much a part as any beam or stanchion in the superstructure. A change in one part of the structure (which includes the soil) affects the other parts, and the passage of time controls changes in the soil.

If the design of the substructure is altered in form or dimension, the behaviour of the soil changes in sympathy. According as the superstructure is sensitive or insensitive to movement, the economy and cost of the design of the substructure vary. If these factors of change and interdependence are forgotten, the decisions taken may, at the best, result in uneconomic design and, at the worst, be the cause of structural damage.

Two examples of this interdependence may suffice to drive home the point that the design is a whole, and that the building and soil must be considered as one unit. A power station stood for years fulfilling its purpose, until cooling water was required, and was pumped from deep aquifers underlying the station. The soil changed its nature under the fresh stresses imposed and serious cracking in the superstructure took place. The second example is that of a hospital which settled badly soon after its construction and sustained extensive and costly damage. The adoption of a raft foundation without sufficient thought being given to the volume of soil which was, in effect, a part of the building was the cause of the failure. A clay layer, lying at a considerable depth and quite unsuspected, had been overstressed, although the strata near the surface were "strong". In both these instances, failure to realise how much of the soil mass was, in fact, part of the building caused unnecessary expense and anxiety. It is quite possible, with knowledge and without great cost, to avoid such damage; it is not so easy to repair it once it has taken place.

1.4. Forms of Foundation Failure

The architect who appreciates the scientific background of the design of foundations, and the principles which govern the behaviour of soils, tries to design the whole complex of soil, substructure and superstructure, as one unit. His object is to ensure that the building will continue to function effectively over its useful life. Failure to command success in this intention is shown by one of two distinct types of movement of the foundation—of the substructure relative to the soil. These are caused by:

(a) A sudden collapse of the soil mass in a catastrophic movement of some magnitude.

(b) A gradual relative movement of parts of the structure, in which movement the time-scale is important. This movement causes increasing distortion of the building.

The first of these types of failure can be exemplified by a stanchion and its footing suddenly sinking into the ground. On account of overstressing of the soil by faulty design of the substructure, a resistance is demanded which the soil is incapable of developing. In some soils, particularly those containing a large proportion of clay, the ability to resist shear (the sliding of one portion of soil on another) is low. Sudden collapse of the soil is caused by a shear failure when sliding takes place and the support is entirely removed from the foundation.

Although sudden collapses of the soil beneath foundations of stanchions are not often recorded, shear failures are by no means uncommon in soil supporting foundation structures. Unsupported slopes, embankments and cuttings are particularly vulnerable and suffer various kinds of shear failure. Support, even by a retaining wall, may not always prevent sudden movement of the soil taking place, for large masses are involved.

The architect of the smaller blocks of flats, the council offices, the swimming pool, the school, will not usually find his foundations suffering a shear failure. But the possibility is present, and he must be able to state with some certainty that, by the application of the principles of soil mechanics to his design, his foundations are protected against such a catastrophe. The best protection is to know and apply the techniques of investigation which can predict the conditions in which shear failure might take place.

1.5. Settlement

Apart from the sudden shear failure of soil, there is a distinct type of failure which is more common and more important. The soil slowly changes in volume under the forces exerted, and the resulting movement causes increasingly pronounced settlement. This movement is initiated by the gradual expulsion of water from the soil. Water can be driven out or abstracted from the soil in various ways:

(a) By the squeezing out of water when the soil is loaded by the weight of a building. This is the most usual cause of settlement.

(b) By the abstraction of water through a disturbance of the soil-water relationship—the excavation of trenches or cuttings, the provision of artificial soil drainage, the pumping of water from aquifers, the planting of fast-growing trees and the exposure of foundation soils for extended periods in times of dry or wet weather are all possible causes of settlement and of movement of the foundation soil.

These changes in the moisture conditions in the soil cause changes in dimensions of that portion of the soil underlying the building. The changes may extend to a great depth, they may be vertical, they may be horizontal, they may be permanently in one direction or reversible as conditions change. Their chief effect may be seen immediately, or may occur only after years have passed since the disturbance of the soil-moisture relationship. The magnitude and distribution of these dimensional changes are dependent on the type of soil and on the nature and distribution of the loads from the building. The mass of soil stressed also has an important influence, and this, in turn, depends on the type of foundation substructure applying the load.

1.6. Designing for Minimum Damage

All buildings distort to some extent, but sometimes the distortion is much greater than is necessary. The architect's aim, so far as foundation design is concerned, is to avoid entirely the type of collapse initiated by sudden shear failure, and to reduce to a minimum the effect of a slow change in soil dimensions. In carrying out this purpose the architect must be ready to adapt the design of the sub-structures and even that of the whole building to achieve the balanced interaction of soil and structure which is the hall-mark of the successful design of foundations. It is not sufficient to design the building and then turn to a belated enquiry into the "strength" of the soil.

To use a simple conception in the face of complexity is dangerous in structural design. On the other hand, a skilled handling of the complexity which does exist in the study of foundations can frequently result in a successful foundation on an apparently "impossible" site. Successful design which eliminates the possibility of shear failure, and takes into account the possible settlement of the foundations, is controlled design. Appreciation of the meaning of the facts available, and the application of the principles outlined in this volume, help to produce controlled design.

To design for minimum damage it is essential that facts are, in fact, available. Site exploration is an essential first step, and should never be omitted from the plan of campaign on the site. The proportion of the cost of any building which must be spent on site investigation is small and brings dividends in the form of greater confidence and guided design.

1.7. Fundamental Study of Soil Behaviour

The last three chapters—Part 3—of this book contain the information most architects want to have at hand. There they will find a discussion of bearing capacity and settlement. The temptation of trying to use these chapters without careful work on the first Parts of the book should be resisted. In fact, the last chapters are written in such a way that the prerequisite knowledge must be readily available to the student of the text. If the architect-reader is to be successful in understanding the role of soils in foundations, he must discipline himself to study what may seem to him to be the unnecessary detail of the earlier part of the book.

It is well known that learning is most effective if there is a short-term objective in view, and if that objective can be seen to be easily attainable. The architect-reader is, therefore, advised to be sure that he understands each chapter before going on to the next. He is also advised to work out afresh each of the problems in the Computation Panels.

The book has been written for two types of reader—the experienced architect who wishes to refresh his knowledge by a general survey of the subject, and the younger man who wishes to get down to detail and calculation. Both approaches are simultaneously and independently possible. An appreciation of all the topics can be made by reading through the chapters. These form a connected sequence in themselves. But, if the reader wishes to go further and to develop some basic skill in foundation design, or to understand more clearly the ideas put before him, he must work through the Computation Panels. These have been kept separate from the text of the chapters in order to avoid any break in continuity for those who wish to obtain the wider view.

1.8. The Plan of the Book

This book consists of three Parts, the first dealing with soil and water and the properties they exhibit without reference to their supporting power in foundations. The second Part discusses the reaction and behaviour of soil under load and measuring of properties related to foundation loading. The third Part discusses how the two main types of failure may be obviated, and shows how the facts and techniques of the first two Parts can be linked in a technique of controlled design of footings.

Much must be taken for granted in a survey of this kind where simplicity of presentation takes an important place. It has been assumed, for example, that the architect is not particularly interested in the techniques of making tests, but only in the values produced from these tests. He is also not likely to carry out a large-scale investigation of the site, but he must understand the significance of the various parts of the report he receives on the site investigation. He is not expected to want to check the reliability of what has been presented in these chapters, so supporting references are not given in detail. Further reading in such periodicals as *Geotechnique* or *Sols* is recommended for those who wish to go further.

Chapter 2

Properties of Soil

2.1. Properties of Importance in Foundation Design

Soil is formed from the decomposition of materials forming the earth's crust. Both the nature of the rock from which the soil is formed and the forces to which the decomposed material has been subjected in geological times have considerable influence on how a soil subsequently behaves. A knowledge of geology is, therefore, of some use to the young architect, and may put him one step ahead in the necessary investigations.

There are two principal ranges of soil properties which come under close scrutiny. These are the agricultural properties (where physics, thermodynamics and biochemistry of the soil are important) and the mechanical properties of the inert soil lying below the agricultural layers. The mechanics of these inert soils form the chief subject of the studies in this volume. There are, of course, instances when the two types overlap; in determining the possibility of driving tractors and other land vehicles over soft surface soil, the mechanics of the soil becomes of more importance than its agricultural properties. It is assumed, however, that the architect is interested only in the static forces in the strata underlying the top soil. Only when great structures, such as massive dams, apply enormous forces need the mechanics of rock be considered. It is assumed, again, that if the architect finds his building can be founded on rock he closes this book with a happy sigh!

In the form most usually encountered in architects' foundations, soil consists of an intimate mixture of solid particles, water and air. The solid particles may be of many different sizes. Both the nature of the soil materials and their proportion in the mass vary, not only from one geological region to another, but also from one part of a site to another. Variation with depth below the surface is also so common that it must be assumed as a normal condition. This factor of variability must always be in the forefront of the mind of

11

the designer. Some variability may not be important and may be accepted without concern. Other kinds of variability, sometimes quite slight, either in nature or location, may produce unfavourable conditions in the foundation soil. The architect must develop a judgement on this point—whether he should ignore the variability he encounters, or should spend time and money eliminating its ultimate effect on the building.

There are two sets of properties which must be investigated. There are, first, the properties of the soil which are inherent in the nature of the soil and are not referred to any ability of the soil to resist load. There are also the mechanical properties which define how a particular soil behaves under load. These latter are determined by applying test loads of various kinds to the soil, and measuring the response in terms of behaviour. The two sets of properties are, of course, mutually related. To an experienced investigator the basic physical properties of the soil can be used to predict the resistance likely to be offered to load. It is unlikely that this estimate would be accepted if unchecked by tests. This chapter deals with the first set of properties only—the basic features of soil structure.

2.2. Classification

Until the 1920's it was imagined that foundation soil was so heterogeneous, and varied so much from point to point both on the surface and in depth, that it would be impossible to develop any general principles of classification and behaviour. In both the 18th and 19th centuries ideal soils (approximating to dry sand) were studied mathematically. Such ideal treatment failed to give the required information about the behaviour of real soil. Many attempts have since been made to obtain a general classification which would help to predict the action of a given soil under load. With the wide experience obtained in foundation design, and from the many researches carried out, several methods have evolved. The behaviour of a foundation soil which has been allocated to a particular classification can now be predicted from the known behaviour of other soils of the same type.

Since the problem is a complex one, classification into broad groups does not provide a sufficiently detailed division to bring to light all the differences between soils. The division into broad groups is, however, a first step, if it is remembered that a change from one group to another should coincide with a distinct change in physical properties. Of all the differing classifications proposed, only one well-known and internationally accepted example is studied below. But in each country there are nationally accepted codes and standards in which similar classification systems are described.

Soil, it has been found, is most accurately and conveniently classified by the sizes of the particles it contains. The most important and broadest divisions into which the material can be separated are *coarse-grained soils* and *fine-grained soils*. The point of division between the two is arbitrary, for soils vary smoothly from one category to another, but it has been found that there are signs of distinct changes in the properties of soils at a particle size of about half a millimetre. In the system described below, a size of 0·6 mm is used. Below this size lie silts and clays (*fine-grained* soils) and above this size lie sands and gravels (*coarse-grained* soils).

The chief difference between the two types is that dry coarse-grained soils depend only on gravity to keep the particles in contact with each other, while individual particles of fine-grained soils are held together by electrostatic forces even when dry. Because of this property, fine-grained soils are often called *cohesive* while coarse-grained soils are called *frictional* or *granular*, referring to the way in which the coarser particles rub against each other.

Granular soils can occur with a range of packing of particles from loose to compact, but whatever the packing, the deformation of such soils under load is relatively slight in comparison with the large movements occurring in cohesive soils. Fine-grained cohesive soils have been laid down by the settling of extremely small particles (one five-hundredth of a millimetre for clays) through still water. Electrostatic forces prevent these small elongated particles from touching each other except perhaps at the ends. If the soil contains much water, the particles may be held completely apart (Fig. 2.1). The texture of saturated fine-grained soils (unlike that of granular soils) encloses relatively large volumes of water-filled spaces which are commonly equal in volume to the volume of the solid particles, and may even be much greater. As an extreme example, the soil on which much of the centre of Mexico City is founded displays only one-seventh of its volume as solid particles, six-sevenths being water-filled spaces. Yet on such unpromising material large buildings are constructed, the whole soil/building complex being considered as one design unit.

Granular soil

Cohesive soils : very fine particles held or repelled by molecular forces

Fig. 2.1. Physical nature of inert soil.

The plasticity of cohesive soils contrasts with the frictional attributes of granular materials. Frictional material naturally offers a greater resistance to pressure and movement than a smooth and plastic soil. Frictional soils, because of the interconnection of the voids between the particles, are highly permeable. Cohesive soils hold their moisture in almost self-contained cavities and offer considerable resistance to the flow of water. These properties are responsible for the diverse reactions of the two types to the movement of water, and to the possibility of change in volume.

But division into only two types does not sufficiently differentiate between the varieties of soil likely to be encountered in foundations. Within each of the two types there are varieties which can be seen to be different, and which exhibit varying properties even on cursory examination. One of the best known systems of separating the cohesive and granular soils into fine classes is that devised by Casagrande. *Casagrande's Classification* (sometimes called the *Unified Soil Classification System*) includes such soils as organic material and peat. Omitting these, there are four symbols to indicate the main divisions of the two broad classes:

G - - - - - - - - Gravel; a particle size which is easily seen. The particles are larger than two millimetres.

S - - - - - - - - Sand; a soil which feels gritty to the fingers and of which most of the particles can be seen without the aid of a magnifier.

M - - - - - - - - Silt; not gritty to the fingers but is still plastic enough to be rolled into threads even when moist. The letter M relates to the Scandinavian word *MO*.

C - - - - - - - - Clay; greasy to the touch. Can be rolled easily into threads when moist. Shrinks on drying. Particles are less than one five-hundredth of a millimetre.

The principal properties of these sub-groups are further indicated by secondary letters:

W - - - - - - - - Well graded   ⎫ These terms are explained
P - - - - - - - - Poorly graded ⎭   below
F - - - - - - - - Excess of fines
L - - - - - - - - Low plasticity
I - - - - - - - - Intermediate plasticity
H - - - - - - - - High plasticity.

The last three refer only to fine-grained soils, for the granular G and S have no plasticity. By putting these letters together, a code is developed which divides inorganic granular soils into eight groups (GW, GC, GP, GF, SW, SC, SP, SF) and cohesive soils into six groups (ML, CL, MI, CI, MH, CH). For example,

GP - - - - - - - - Gravel-sand mixture; little or no fines
SC - - - - - - - - Sand-clay mixtures; excellent binder
CH - - - - - - - - Clay of high plasticity; a "fat" clay.

But even these 14 groups do not classify foundation soils into all the possible categories. It is possible to find two soils, both in the same classification, which have widely varying properties. All possible studies must therefore be made of behaviour as related to soil type. The young architect is advised to keep full notes of foundation conditions. Reports on site investigations are not of much value if they are interpreted wrongly.

2.3. Particle-size Analysis

The particles in a particular sample of soil may vary widely in size from gravel to the microscopic flakes which comprise a clay. The variations in the sizes of particles and the proportion of the total sample represented by each size are valuable indicators of how the soil will behave under the load of a foundation. For example, if many particle sizes are represented, the soil will be expected to compact well and to be stable. The smaller sizes of particles nest between the larger, and offer greater frictional resistance to movement. Such a soil will be less likely to suffer sudden failure or to settle as time passes than a soil containing only one size of particle. Because a soil with many different particle sizes represented shows such valuable properties it is said to show a *good grading* or to be *well-graded* (W in the soil classification system discussed above). Soils, on the other hand, which contain only a few different particle sizes cannot be trusted to support loads so effectively. They are *poorly-graded* (P in Casagrande's classification). They fail to compact well, especially when dry. Sea sand, for example, is usually poorly graded. It will not compact to any extent nor will it easily bear a heavy load. The same strictures apply to gravel consisting of a uniform size of stone, but if gravel of several sizes is mixed with sand and clay the presence of many particle sizes gives improved compaction and bearing capacity. In the south of England a naturally occurring material of this kind, called "hoggin", is much sought after for embankments and foundations.

It is important, therefore, for the architect to appreciate the meaning of a *particle-size analysis*—the distribution pattern of grain sizes throughout the soil. It is not too much to say that a glance at a curve showing particle-size analysis (usually called a *grading curve*) gives a good indication of the problems likely to be encountered. Its message can aid the architect in his design and guide him more effectively than any site visit or visual inspection can possibly do, if unsupported by classification and grading tests.

The *Particle-size Analysis Chart* shows particle size plotted against the proportion (by weight) of the dried sample which consists of sizes smaller than the chosen diameter of particle. On the standard chart:

(a) The range of size from 200 mm to less than 0·002 mm is set off so that equal divisions along the horizontal axis represents an equal *multiplication* of the particle size. Reference to Fig. 2.2 shows that the multiplier in this instance is approximately three. It is not of significance that the figure is not exactly three, as the derivation of a grading curve gives only an approximate relationship between the various contents of particle sizes. The horizontal scale in the chart is, in fact, a logarithmic scale.

(b) The percentages, measured by the ordinates, are on a natural scale, where each equal division represents an equal *addition* to the values. Each point on the grading curve represents the proportion of the weight of the test sample which consists entirely of particles of a smaller diameter than the one indicated on the horizontal scale by the point chosen.

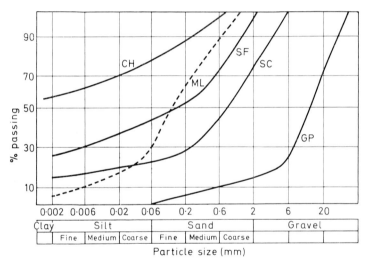

Fig. 2.2.   Particle size analysis of five types of soil.

2.4. *Interpretation of Grading Curves*

In Fig. 2.2, five grading curves are shown, together with the possible classification of the soils under the Casagrande system. If each of these is taken in turn, the lessons of interpretation of the grading curves are illustrated by example.

Soil GP: This material was being considered and tested for its suitability for building an embankment. About 75% of the weight of the material consists of particles greater than 6 mm (or ($\frac{1}{4}$ inch). This can be checked by running a horizontal line from the 25% mark. The line intersects the grading curve at about 6 mm. The first lesson to be learnt is, thus, that a steep portion of the curve indicates a relative abundance of the material within that zone. Conversely, a flat portion of the curve indicates a paucity of material of these sizes. On this curve, for example, there is a relatively flat portion between 2 mm and 6 mm. This means that nearly the same amount of material passes through the successive sieves, and thus little or nothing can be trapped and left behind. The curve is also well over to the right of the chart, indicating a coarser material.

Soil SC: This curve shows a soil having about 25% in the gravel range. The horizontal line through the 75% mark cuts the curve on the 2 mm ordinate, and the portion lying above this represents small gravel. Through the sand portion all sizes of particles are represented, but there is a relative absence of silt. A terminal 15% of clay is shown. Such a sand-clay mixture could act as a binder, and compact well.

Soil ML: About 70% of this material lies in the sand range chiefly in the fine sand region. Most of the rest of the particles are of the silt sizes. This could be called a silty sand, or a silty fine sand, since the steepest portion of the curve lies in the fine sand range.

Soil SF: The grading curve here has no steep portion, and many sizes are represented through both sands and silts. About 60% of the material is fine sand, silt and clay, and, of that, about one-half is clay. This is a sand with an excess of fines; it could be called a clayey sand.

Soil CH: Here is a material containing 60% clay. It is worth noting that the finer the material, the more the grading curve rises and moves to the left. Although 40% is coarser than the clay-particle size, the soil shows all the characteristics of a clay. In relation to their concentration in the sample, the finer particles always have a greater influence on the properties and behaviour of the soil than do the coarser particles. In fact, any soil with more than 30% clay particles should be expected to behave as a clay. Because of the high concentration of fine particles this material has a high plasticity.

In becoming familiar with the meaning of each grading curve, the architect should be careful to keep his conditions of observation constant. The shape of the chart, for example, should not be altered. He should become accustomed to the visual shape of the curves and be able to interpret them without more than a cursory glance at the values of abscissae and ordinates. This cannot be done if the scales of the chart do not remain constant. The proportion of approximately 1 : 2 between the height and length of the chart should be maintained to allow of intuitive appreciation of the meanings of the grading curves. Some simple size relationships can also be memorised. For example the values 10, 1, 0·1 and 0·01 mm are the mean sizes of Medium Gravel, Coarse Sand, Fine Sand and Medium Silt. By the time 0·001 mm is reached, the material is well into the clay range.

2.5. Moisture Content

In addition to its content of particles, the soil also contains water. One of the most important characteristics of foundations is the quantity of water present in the soil. If all the voids are filled with water, the soil is said to be *saturated*. If only some of the voids are filled with water, and some contain air, the soil is *unsaturated*. Most soils encountered by architects in their foundations are saturated, and it is to these soils that attention will be paid here.

Free water and water molecules are contained in the soil in several ways, but for the purpose of this discussion it can be agreed that there are two types of water to be considered—*free water* and *held water*. The held water, as its name implies, does not flow under the action of gravity, but is held tightly to the soil particles by molecular forces. The heating of a sample of soil at 105–110° C drives off the *free water* and some of the more loosely bound *held water* and leaves a dry sample. Any higher temperature might disrupt the minerals of the soil by driving off the water of crystallization. The estimation of the moisture content, the water driven off at the above temperature, is one of the important determinations which must be carried out during a site investigation. It can be determined quickly by a number of methods, and by probes inserted into the soil. The most reliable, although time-consuming, method is that of drying and weighing. The proportion of water in the soil is expressed as a percentage of the *dry* weight of the soil and is represented by *m*.

2.6. Pores and Voids

A common method of studying a soil is to imagine the solid particles fused into one solid block with no voids, the rest of the space representing the remainder of the original volume of the sample, being empty voids, or voids filled with water. Figure 2.3 illustrates this technique, and compares a typical cohesive soil with a typical granular soil. The voids in the clay together represent a volume approximately equal to the volume of solids, while in the granular soil, because of the closer packing of the particles in the original material, less space is left when these particles are fused solid, and the proportion of voids to solids is less.

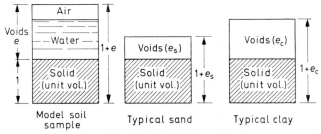

Fig. 2.3.   Composition of soil types.

The ratio of the *volume* of voids to the *volume* of solids in known as the *void ratio*. In the internationally accepted range of symbols this is represented by e. The value of the void ratio itself gives an indication of the type of soil and of the latent possibility, for example, of settlement. It also gives some indication of the porosity of the soil, but must not be confused with it. In the accepted sense of the term, porosity represents the ratio of the *volume* of voids to the *total volume*. From Fig. 2.3, if the volume of the solids is assumed to be unity, we have

$$\text{Void ratio} = \frac{\text{Volume of voids}}{\text{Volume of solids}} = \frac{e}{1} = e$$

$$\text{Porosity} = \frac{\text{Volume of voids}}{\text{Total volume}} = \frac{e}{1+e} = n.$$

The void ratio is the more generally used of the two quantities and is much more useful in calculation than is the value of porosity.

It should be remembered that the void ratio is not a fundamental property of the soil, but rather is indicative of its condition at the time of test. Soils may have their void ratios changed by pressure or by vibration or other disturbance, and the same material may appear with quite different porosities. If, for example, a soil is imagined to consist entirely of spheres of equal size, and that these are balanced in the loosest formation, the voids represent about 48% of the total volume (or a void ratio of about 0·92). If the spheres nest into each other to give the densest packing possible, the volume of voids is only 28% of the total volume, or a void ratio of 0·39. The frictional soils— sands and gravels—can also show variations in packing which result in different proportions of voids for the same material. For natural sands the proportion of voids is not likely to be so high as for a block of uniform spheres. For cohesive soils, consolidation under load reduces the void ratio at rates the determination of which is very important in the study of possible settlement of foundations.

2.7. Density

The density of the soil, measured as its weight per unit of volume, is clearly an important property. Special figures, however, must be obtained for comparison and calculation. This necessitates the study, not only of the mass of soil as obtained in sample form from a site, but also of the separate properties of the soil structure.

From whatever source or parent material the soil is derived, it is composed of three *phases*: inert particles, moisture and gas. For the purposes of foundation design it may be assumed that the moisture is pure water, and that the gas is air. This assumption is justified when considering only the mechanical properties of the soil. The mineral particles of the soil have a specific gravity of nearly 2·7; they are heavier than water by this factor. For special calculations the specific gravity of the particles should be determined, but for trial calculations the figure of from 2·6 to 2·7 may be assumed. Water always has a specific gravity of unity, or weighs 1·0 gram per millilitre.

On the site, the mineral particles are dispersed throughout the volume of soil, the water and air being assumed to be approximately evenly distributed throughout the voids. As was described in the previous section, the normal method of studying the soil is to imagine the mineral particles fused into a solid mass, and the water and air to form separate volumes. From this conception it is easily possible to obtain the values of the two important measures of density—the *bulk density* and the *dry density*.

Bulk density is obtained by dividing the total weight of the sample as obtained from the site by its volume. The result may be given in various units such as lb/ft^3, but the value which is most useful in calculation is described in g/ml. This figure represents the density of the soil as it occurs in nature and the international symbol used to designate it is the Greek letter gamma (γ).

Dry density is found by dividing the weight of the sample, after being dried, by its original volume. Since air has no weight (for the purposes of foundation studies) and the water has been driven off, the dry density gives a measure of the dispersion of the solid matter through the mass of soil. The weight of the solids divided by the original volume would be 2·7 g/ml if there were no air and no water originally. The amount by which the dry density is less than this figure shows how widely the solid particles are dispersed, or, alternatively, how great a proportion of the whole volume was occupied by air and water. The standard symbol for this figure is γ_d. A useful relationship, which applies to all soils, is

$$\gamma_d = \gamma(1-m).$$

2.8. Limits of Consistency

One of the characteristics of fine-grained cohesive soils is plasticity, the ability of the particles to cohere together, and to form with the free and held water a plastic and mouldable whole. It is important to determine, for cohesive soils in foundations, the limits between which they remain plastic. These limits, in turn, depend on the previous history of the soil and on the mineral composition of the particles it contains. The values obtained in tests form a secondary technique in the classification of cohesive soils. It is quite possible, once the grading curve lies in the left-hand portion of the particle-size analysis chart, for two soils with apparently the same analysis to have different characteristics. The study of the limits of plasticity or consistency enables the architect to separate two such soils into their correct categories and to predict more accurately how they will behave.

As plasticity is controlled by the amount of water contained in the sample, there are three values of moisture content which give valuable indications of the possible behaviour of the soil. These are the *natural moisture content* of the soil as it exists in the foundation, and the two limits of consistency—the *liquid limit* (a higher moisture content) and the *plastic limit* (a lower moisture content). Between these two limits, the soil is in a plastic state, and the range between the two values gives a measure of the stability of the soil. This range is called the *plasticity index*. If this is a narrow range, then any change in moisture content may either cause the clay to become liquid (above the liquid limit) or to become so dry as to cease to be plastic (below the plastic limit). If the range is a wide one, there is not so much danger of a change in moisture content having a catastrophic effect. The relationship of the natural moisture content to the two limits also shows how close the soil is to losing plasticity and to becoming very wet (and weak) or dry and non-plastic.

The value of the plasticity index also gives a clue as to the type of soil. The wider the range between the plastic and liquid limits the finer the soil; both plastic and liquid limits also show increases as the soil becomes finer, the liquid limit usually increasing faster than the plastic limit. Coarse silts have low consistency limits, and, like sands, have no plasticity index, or one which is so narrow in range as to be, in practice, equivalent to zero.

The experimental methods employed to determine the liquid limit (LL) and the plastic limit (PL) are internationally accepted, although quite empirical. It is not necessary for the architect to be able to carry out the tests (which, in fact, require considerable practice if they are to be repeatable) but he must understand the significance of the figures, especially as they are so important in secondary classification.

At the liquid limit the particles are artificially dispersed within the mass of soil, supported by an excess of water. As the water dries out, the change in volume which takes place is one of moisture loss only. The loss of moisture is thus equal to the loss of volume. If a graph of moisture content against the volume of the sample is con-

structed, the slope of the line below the liquid limit is at 45°. Every
millilitre or cubic inch of moisture lost results in an equal loss in
volume. As this loss continues, the clay particles are drawn closer
together (Fig. 2.4).

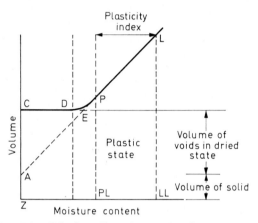

Fig. 2.4.   Cohesive soils: volume and moisture content.

There must be a limit to this process, and there finally occurs,
during the drying of the sample, a moisture content beyond which the
particles cannot be compressed together any more. At this point the
clay changes colour, for the drying process, still going on, results in
water being drawn out from the material without any closing up of
the clay particles. Water leaves the surface, but the volume remains
constant and cracks appear, as strong electrostatic forces between the
clay minerals resist any further decrease in volume. This moisture
content is known as the *shrinkage limit*, although it is not of such
value in calculation as the other two values. Figure 2.4, however,
gives some interesting facts about particular clays which have gone
through this drying process.

If, for example, it were possible to avoid the horizontal part of
the curve in Fig. 2.4, and to continue to find the volume of the clay
reducing at the same rate as the extraction of water, then an extension
of line LP to the zero line of moisture content would give the value of
the volume of the sample with no voids or moisture—the volume of

the solids as fused into one mass (Fig. 2.3). This value of the volume of the solids is shown by AZ. Since line APL is at 45°, CE and AC are equal. In other words, the proportion of water in the sample at the shrinkage limit is numerically equal to the volume of voids in the sample in the dried state.

The most important assistance which can be given by the limits of consistency is to separate and classify soils of the cohesive type (the soils which give rise to difficult conditions in foundations) more exactly than can be done by mere particle-size analysis. Fig. 2.5 shows

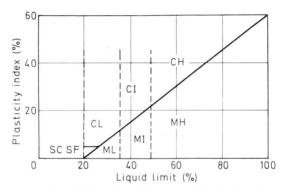

Fig. 2.5. Simplified version of Casagrande's plasticity chart.

the plasticity chart devised by Casagrande. Clays lie above the inclined line, and silts below, assuming that only inorganic material is in question. (Organic material in a foundation should be avoided or removed. Usually it can be detected by its dark colour and by its smell, especially when heated.) This chart gives a further method of ensuring that an accurate classification is given to a cohesive soil, and, once the classification is established, the possible behaviour of the soil can be predicted with some accuracy.

Method of attack

(1) Draw up Table CP2A taking care that the lines in columns (2) and (5) are staggered to record the weights retained *between* sieves.

(2) The total weight of the sample from soil A is 202 g. Column (2) shows that nothing is left on the 6-mm sieve, thus the amount passing that sieve is 202 g. There is a weight of 50 g left on the 2-mm sieve; thus $202 - 50 = 152$ g is passed through. The whole of columns (3) and (6) are completed in this way. It then only remains for the figures in columns (3) and (6) to be converted into percentages of the respective weights of the samples, (4) and (7). The values towards the bottom of columns (2) and (5) would not be obtained by physical sieving, but by other means such as sedimentation.

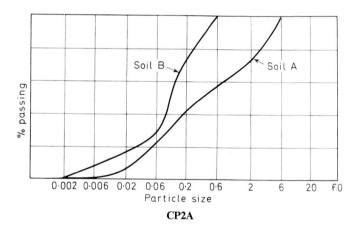

CP2A

(3) From columns (4) and (7), Fig. CP2A is constructed and the following conclusions can be drawn.

Soil A. This is a well-graded soil; the line passes through five of the spaces in the diagram. It is also granular. Only 24% has particle sizes smaller than fine sand. There is a weight of 21% of coarse silt, but only 3% is finer than this.

Soil B. This is steeply graded in the medium and fine sand range and the finest 29% is of silt, there being 12% of the fine-silt size, but no clay particles.

(4) Many other considerations would have to be taken into account before a final decision could be made—state of compaction,

pore-pressure and water table conditions. On the evidence of the particle-size analysis alone, however, the well-graded granular soil would be preferred to the finer, poorly graded material because of its relative freedom from settlement and its ability to develop higher shear strengths under foundation loads.

CP2B
PROBLEM: To determine the properties of a saturated soil from wet and dried samples

Data
The sample, as extracted from the site, weighed 19·05 g and after drying, 14·40 g.

Result required
(a) The void ratio of the sample.
(b) The moisture content.

Method of attack
(1) Draw up Table CP2B where the weights and volumes of solids, water and air can be systematically determined. The data supplied or assumed are underlined. The rest is calculated.
(2) The weight of water driven off (g) is numerically equal to its volume (ml).
(3) The weight of solids is the dry weight of the sample, and the volume of the solid particles obtained by dividing by the specific gravity.
(4) The void ratio is the ratio of voids (or the space occupied by water in a saturated soil) to solids. This is $4·65/5·32 = 0·87$.

Table CP2B

Phase	Weight (g)	Volume (ml)
Air	Zero	Zero (saturated soil)
Water	$19·05 - 14.40 = 4.65$	4.65
Solid	14·40	$14·40/2·71 = 5·32$

(5) From Table CP2B the weight of water is 4·65 g. The moisture content is calculated as the ratio of the weight of water to the weight of solids, or $4·65/14·40 = 0·32$ or 32%.

PROBLEM: To estimate the moisture content of a saturated soil without drying

Data
The sample of soil is a clay and is known to have a void ratio of 1·21.

Result required
The moisture content of the soil.

Method of attack
(1) The soil is known to be saturated. *In these circumstances only*, the void ratio is equal to the moisture content multiplied by the specific gravity of the particles.

(2) Thus the moisture content of a saturated soil can be estimated by dividing the void ratio by the specific gravity

$$m = 1·21/2·7 = 0·45 \text{ or } 45\%.$$

The specific gravity is an assumed figure. It usually lies between 2·6 and 2·7.

PROBLEM: To estimate the void ratio of an unsaturated soil

Data
The degree of saturation is 0·65. The bulk density of soil as measured on the site is 135 lb/ft^3. The moisture content is 16%.

Result required
(a) The void ratio of the soil.
(b) An opinion on the type of soil this is likely to be.

Method of attack

(1) Draw up Table CP2D so that the properties of the phases in the soil can be systematically evaluated. The data supplied or assumed are underlined. The other figures are calculated. Draw the model soil sample.

(2) If the soil has a degree of saturation of 0·65, then the voids are filled to 65 % of their volume with water, and 35 % with air.

(3) The weight of the model soil sample is thus $2·7 + 0·65e$ grams, for air has no weight.

(4) The volume of the model soil sample is $1 + e$.

(5) The density of the sample is thus (weight divided by volume)

$$\frac{2·7 + 0·65e}{1 + e}.$$

(6) But this density, in cgs units, can be obtained from the bulk density by dividing by the density of water. Density $= 135/62·4 = 2·16$

(7) By equating the figures in (5) and (6) the void ratio is found

$$2·16 = \frac{2·7 + 0·65e}{1 + e}$$
$$e = 0·33.$$

(8) Such a void ratio, coupled with the bulk density measured, suggests a dense sand.

Table CP2D

Phase	Weight (g)	Volume (ml)	Density (g/ml)
Air	Zero	$0·35e$	Zero
Water	$0·16 \times 2·7 = 0·43$	$0·43$	$1·0$
Solid	$2·7$	$1·0$	$2·7$
Sample	$2·7 + 0·65e$	$1 + e$	$135/62·4 = 2·16$

CP2E

PROBLEM: To determine whether a soil is saturated, and if unsaturated to estimate the values of the soil properties

Data

The weight of the sample was 17·70 g and, after drying, 15·25 g. Its volume when moist was 10·55 ml.

Results required

    (a) Degree of saturation.
    (b) Moisture content.
    (c) Void ratio.
    (d) Bulk density.
    (e) Dry density.

Method of attack

(1) Draw up Table CP2E and sketch the model soil sample showing air and water in the void space.

(2) The total volume of the sample is 10·55 ml, but solids and water occupy only 8·10 ml. Air is, therefore, present to the extent of 10·55 − 8·10 = 2·45 ml. The total volume of voids is 10·55 − 5·65 = 4·90 ml. Thus the degree of saturation is (4·90 − 2·45)/4·90 = 0·5 or 50%.

(3) From Table CP2E, the weight of water is 2·45 g and the weight of solids 15·25 g. Thus moisture content = 0·16 or 16%.

(4) From (2) the volume of voids is 4·90 ml. The volume of solids, from the table, is 5·65 ml. Void ratio = 4·90/5·65 = 0·87.

(5) Bulk density is weight/volume or 17·70/10·55 = 1·68 g/ml or 1·68 × 62·4 = 105 lb/ft^3.

(6) Dry density can be obtained from the weight of solids divided by total volume = 15·25/10·55 = 1·45 or 1·45 × 62·4 = 90·5 lb/ft^3.

The dry density can also be obtained from the moisture content.

$$\gamma = \gamma_d(1+m) \text{ or } 1·68 = 1·16\,\gamma_d$$
$$\gamma_d = 1·45.$$

Table CP2E

Phase	Weight (g)	Volume (ml)	Density (g/ml)
Air	Zero	2·45	Zero
Water	$17·70 - 15·25 = 2·45$	2·45	1·0
Solid	15·25	$\dfrac{15·25}{2·70} = 5·65$	2·7
Sample	17·70	10·55	1·68

CP2F

PROBLEM: To estimate the change in void ratio suffered by a sample compressed under a load

Data

A sample of soil was extracted from a site by a sharp-edged cylindrical core cutter of 1/30 cubic foot in volume. The weight of the sample was 4·07 lb. A smaller portion weighing 25·34 g was dried to a weight of 21·31 g. The rest of the sample in the core cutter was cut down to a height of 4 inches. It was then loaded, still in the core cutter, under a constant pressure from a plunger which fitted the core cutter. When the consolidation of the soil had ceased, the depth of the sample was found to be 3·90 inches.

Results required

(a) Void ratio of the original sample.
(b) Degree of saturation of the original sample.
(c) Change in void ratio due to consolidation.

Method of attack

(1) Construct Table CP2F so that the properties of the soil may be systematically determined. Values measured from the sample are underlined.

(2) The bulk density of the soil is $4·07 \times 30$ (lb/ft^3) since the large sample was 1/30 ft^3 in volume. Bulk density is, therefore, 122·1 lb/ft^3 or $122·1/62·4 = 1·96$ g/ml.

(3) The volume of the small sample is thus $25\cdot34/1\cdot96$ (ml) since there are $1\cdot96$ g for each ml of the original soil. Volume $= 12\cdot93$ ml.

(4) The volume of solids and water amounts to $11\cdot92$ ml. The volume of air is thus $12\cdot93 - 11\cdot92 = 1\cdot01$ ml. Total voids are $5\cdot04$ ml and the void ratio $e = 5\cdot04/7\cdot89 = 0\cdot64$.

(5) The degree of saturation is given by the ratio of volume of water to volume of voids. $s = 4\cdot03/5\cdot04 = 0\cdot80$ or 80%.

(6) The sample changes from $4\cdot0$ inches thick to $3\cdot9$ inches, the other dimensions remaining the same. This is accomplished by the driving out of air and water, the volume of solid particles being unchanged. The volume change is $(4\cdot0-3\cdot9)/4\cdot0 = 0\cdot025$ or $2\cdot5\%$. Total volume is $(1+e)$. Change is $(1+0\cdot64)(0\cdot025) = 0\cdot04$. New void ratio $= 0\cdot64 - 0\cdot04 = 0\cdot60$.

Table CP2F

Phase	Weight (g)	Volume (ml)	Density (g/ml)
Air	Zero	$1\cdot01$	Zero
Water	$25\cdot34 - 21\cdot31 = 4\cdot03$	$4\cdot03$	$1\cdot0$
Solid	$21\cdot31$	$21\cdot31/2\cdot7 = 7.89$	$2\cdot7$
Sample	$25\cdot34$	$12\cdot93$	$\dfrac{4\cdot07 \times 30}{62\cdot4} = 1\cdot96$

CP2G

PROBLEM: To study the characteristics of cohesive soils and make decisions on their classification and suitability as foundations

Data

The table gives some data collected on sites. Fill in the values and statements in the spaces indicated by question marks.

Results required

Comments on these figures obtained from site investigations. The behaviour of the soils in foundations should be estimated.

Soil	Moisture content (mean of several samples) m (%)	Void ratio at			LL (%)	PL (%)	PI (%)	Comments
		LL	PL	m				
1	20	1·00	?	0·54	37	?	24	?
2	35	1·67	0·86	0·94	62	?	?	Hand sample appears to be CH material
3	22	0·75	0·67	0·65	28	24	?	?
4	39	1·40	?	1·05	52	Varying 37–27 with depth	?	?
5	?	0·49	?	0·52	18	?	32	Hand sample is a fine sand

Method of attack

(1) Use the Plasticity Chart, and take note of the relationship of the natural moisture content to the LL and PL. The void ratio of the soil on the site gives an indication of its degree of saturation.

(2) *Soil 1*: The plastic limit is $37 - 24 = 13\%$ and the chart shows that this is probably a clay with intermediate plasticity. The natural moisture content is well within the plastic range, and the void ratio shows that the soil is saturated ($e = mG_s$ for saturated soil; $0·54 = 20\% \times 2·7$).

(3) *Soil 2*: The evidence here confirms the assessment made from the hand sample. The soil at plastic limit is, of course, saturated, so the void ratio shows that the PL is approximately 32% ($m = e/G_s = 0·86/2·7$). Particular study of the consolidation characteristics of this soil is desirable.

(4) *Soil 3*: The PI is 4% and the soil is probably a silt of low plasticity. Silts are likely to cause difficulties in a foundation and are subject to frost heave. The void ratio at natural moisture content is higher than would be expected for a saturated soil at a moisture content of 22%. The soil is, therefore, unsaturated and the natural moisture content is lower than the plastic limit. This foundation would require a much more thorough study before the footings are designed.

(5) *Soil 4*: The mean moisture content is a little above the highest value of plastic limit and the soil is thus likely to be plastic, but not wet in appearance. The soil is apparently a silt of high plasticity. As

the PI increases, strength also increases and permeability and rate of the consolidation decrease. These facts have been determined by observation of many soils. In this instance as depth increases the valuable properties of the soil improve. The foundation should be placed as deep as is economically justified. In view also of the nature of the soil, this is a case where the construction of a basement might be helpful (see chapter on Bearing Capacity).

(6) *Soil 5*: The only thing which can be said here is that the soil must be re-examined. A fine sand cannot have a PI of 32%. Some mistake has been made in the testing procedure. The soil is suspect for it is clearly very wet, having a natural moisture content (19%) above the liquid limit ($m = e/G_s$). A fine wet sand can produce difficulties.

Chapter 3

Above and Below the Water Table

3.1 The Water Table

In Chapter 2 the occurrence of water as one of the phases of soil is studied. The amount of water and its distribution in the pores is one of the fundamental properties of the soil. Water, however, is not merely present in the soil as an inert part of the structure. Because of its lack of shear strength, water can flow in the soil; it can produce pressures which, unless controlled, can be deleterious to the functioning of structures depending on the strength of soil. The effect which water has, both above and below the water table, and the significance of the term *water table* itself, are subjects of importance in foundation design.

Conditions in the soil can, perhaps, be fairly represented by a simple example from everyday experience. Imagine a pad of blotting paper several inches thick. It is sawn through in a vertical direction, but the cut edges are held together. The whole pad is then immersed in a dish containing about an inch of water. We all know what happens; the water soaks up into the blotting paper, and more water has to be added to the dish to maintain the one inch level round the block of blotting paper. After a time, the movement of the water into the pad ceases and a state of equilibrium is reached. No more water will be required to maintain the level. Imagine now that the pad of paper is thick enough so that the upper surface remains dry. The two cut edges are now imagined to be drawn apart. If we look down between them we can see the light reflected in the surface of the water about an inch above the base of the dish. We know quite well that the blotting paper above this level is just as wet as the blotting paper below, and that the dampness will gradually decrease as the height above the water surface increases. The level at which the water can be seen is known as the *water table*. This is an inappropriate name, since it gives the impression that the water table is a level surface. The water table is not necessarily flat; on many sites it will be found to have a distinct slope. In Fig. 3.1 the contours of the water table on a site surveyed by the author are shown. This shows a gradually dropping level, which is not in any sense like a "table". A better term to describe this level at which the water can be seen in boreholes is the *phreatic surface*. The result of the survey shown in this Figure necessitated a complete change in the type of foundation from that originally planned.

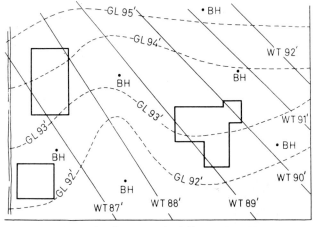

Fig. 3.1.   Contours of a falling water table.

The important fact to remember is that the phreatic surface is the level, at any point on the site, at which the pressure in the water is zero (or atmospheric). Above this level, the pressure in the water in the soil is a negative or suction pressure and is sufficient to lift the water above the water table. Below the phreatic surface, the pressure in the water (known as *pore pressure*) is positive or compressive. This idea of pressure in the water, and pressure which increases with the depth of the water, is familiar, especially to those who have done any skin diving. The rate at which pore pressure in the soil increases as the depth below the water table increases is the same as the rate of increase of the pressure in a freshwater lake or river—one gram per centimetre square, per centimetre of depth, or 62·4 lb/ft^2 per foot of depth. This rule applies for any soil over the whole range from clay to gravel.

Above the water table, on the other hand, other circumstances come into play. The extent to which water is lifted by suction through the fine spaces in the soil, that is, by *capillary action*, depends on the diameters of the tubes or pore-sizes in the soil. The smaller the diameter of these pores, the higher is the *capillary fringe* (or volume of dampened soil) above the level of zero water pressure (the phreatic surface). For example, sands and gravels, having very large individual voids, show almost no capillary fringe, whereas the finer-grained soils, although possessing greater total voids, have these voids distributed through very fine pores, and may show a high capillary fringe.

3.2. Intergranular and Pore Pressure

The effect of pore pressure on the pressure between the particles of the soil—the *intergranular pressure*—depends on whether the particles lie above or below the phreatic surface. Figure 3.2 gives an

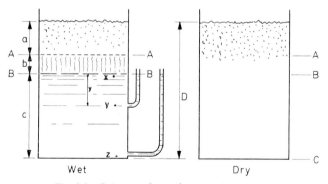

Fig. 3.2. Intergranular and pore-water pressure.

illustration of how pressures vary according to the position of the water table. The two containers are equal in all dimensions, and originally contain the same weight of soil in the same condition. The pressure on the bottom of each container when the soil is dry is thus equal to the dry density of the soil multiplied by its depth. The dry density (γ_d) is measured, let us say, in gram/ml and the depth (D) in cm. Thus the pressure on every square centimetre of the bottom of the cylinder is $\gamma_d D$ g/cm^2 in both vessels. In the same way, if the dry density is measured in lb/ft^3 and the depth in feet, the pressure on the bottom is in lb/ft^2.

If, now, water is poured into the first cylinder, assuming that all air can be expelled, and the conditions allowed to settle down so that the capillary fringe is formed and reaches equilibrium, we have two vessels of the same size but with differing pressures in the soil. In the dry cylinder, pressures are all intergranular; each particle presses on those around and below it, and the final summation of pressure at the bottom is simply calculated, as was done above. In the wet container, however, although the addition of the water merely fills the empty voids in the soil, expelling the air and causing no change in volume, three layers have been developed. The first, from the surface to the letter A, consists of dry soil. The second, from the letter A to the letter B, consists of soil saturated by capillary water, and the third, from letter B to letter C, consists of soil saturated by water below the water table. At the level B, there is no visible difference between the state of the soil just above and just below the water table (B) or phreatic surface, but the state of pressure above is negative, and that below positive. The capillary fringe will, in practice, not stop abruptly at the letter A but, for the sake of illustration, it can be assumed that from A to C the soil is saturated, but in two different ways.

In the capillary fringe, from A to B, the water is held above the water table by suction, which means by tension in the water itself. The water is rather in the same situation as a cage in a pit shaft. The cage is hung in a vertical tube, the cage and its supporting cable being in tension. This tension is transferred as a compression applied to the walls of the shaft, and so into the soil through which the shaft is driven. The presence of the cage and cable in tension adds a further compression or intergranular pressure in the soil. Similarly, water suspended in the pores of the soil is in tension, and transmits this tension as a compression into the grains of the soil.

Below the water table, conditions are simpler. As the depth increases below B, the weight of the soil particles and the weight of the water which inundates the soil and fills the voids, both increase. The total pressure therefore increases with depth. It can be imagined that, from the water table downwards, there are two ways in which

Table 3A

1 Level	2 Total depth	3 Total pressure ("wet" case)	4 Pore pressure ("wet" case)	5 Effective or intergranular pressure ("wet" case) Col. 3 minus Col. 4	6 Effective or intergranular pressure = total pressure ("dry" case)
A	a	$\gamma_d\, a$	—	$\gamma_d a$	$\gamma_d a$
B	$a+b$	$\gamma_d a + \gamma b$	Zero	$\gamma_d a + \gamma b$	$\gamma_d(a+b)$
C	$a+b+c$	$\gamma_d a + \gamma(b+c)$	$+ c\gamma_w$	$\gamma_d a + \gamma(b+c) - \gamma_w c$	$\gamma_d(a+b+c)$ or $\gamma_d D$

the weight of the saturated soil is being transmitted downwards to the level C. First, there is the intergranular pressure where the particles touch each other. This pressure carries the weight of the soil downwards. There is also the pore pressure. The water, acting quite independently and passing between the particles, through the pores of the soil, carries its own weight down to C as a pore pressure. An example illustrates the method of obtaining information about pressures in the soil on a site.

Figure 3.2 is used to construct Table 3A from the following argument:

Level A: Here, the depth is a and the dry density is γ_d. The pressure in both the "wet" and the "dry" containers is, therefore, the same and equal to the product of the dry density and the depth ($\gamma_d a$).

Level B: Here, the pressure consists of that transferred from level A together with the pressures developed between A and B. The total pressure consists of the weight of a depth a of dry soil, and the weight of a depth b of saturated soil of bulk density γ. Column 3 of Table 3A gives the final result. Since B is the water table, the pore pressure at that level is zero. The water above the level B is "hung" in the pores of the soil, and exerts no pore pressure at B although there is no visible difference in appearance of the soil just above or just below the phreatic surface; both levels are saturated. Again, therefore, the intergranular pressure at B is equal to the total pressure, but this figure is different for the "wet" and "dry" case.

Level C: At the bottom of the container, the pore pressure is the product of the density of water and its depth. The total pressure is again given in Column 3. The intergranular pressure is the difference between the total and pore pressures, and this value is given in Column 5 for the "wet" case. For the "dry" case, the total and the intergranular pressures are the same, but are much more simply obtained since there is no pore pressure. Work through this conception carefully, and calculate the numerical examples in the Computation Panel.

Since the strength of a soil to resist loading by a building depends on the contact and friction between particles, the intergranular pressure is usually called the *effective pressure* or *effective stress*. The water in the soil cannot provide any resistance to deformation, and the pore pressure is sometimes called the *neutral pressure*. In fact, its presence reduces the value of the intergranular pressure as can be understood from Table 3A and from the Computation Panel for this chapter.

3.3. Energy of Water

By virtue of the fact that it can flow (because it develops no shear strength) water possesses energy of various kinds. This energy can be destructive, or can be controlled to produce, for example, power in a hydroelectric scheme. Water in the pores of a foundation soil also possesses energy. If this fact is not recognized and the energy of the water controlled or directed, damage may well ensue to the foundation or to any accumulation of fine particles subjected to pore pressure. Buildings can be cracked, or hillsides can begin to move. Floors of basements may heave up and other accidents occur if the architect fails to allow for the energy of the water in the soil. It is important therefore that, in addition to being able to distinguish between total, pore and effective pressures, the architect should be able to understand how the energy in the soil can be directed and made harmless or even helpful.

Water possesses three types of energy. The first is *potential energy* or *position energy*. This can be appreciated intuitively if one sees a dam perched high up on a hillside. We can visualize the energy of this water if it were released, and the damage it can cause. The second type of energy possessed by the water is *velocity energy*, as exemplified by the jet from a fire hose, and the third is *pressure energy* which is not so easily visualized, but can be illustrated by trying to hold back the water in the kitchen tap with the thumb!

The ground water, the water in soil, possesses all these three types of energy, but to different extents. Any movement of the water through the soil is important and must be carefully considered, but the velocity by which such movement occurs is generally so small that the velocity energy of the ground water is insignificant and can be neglected in any assessment of total energy. We are thus left with only two types of energy in the ground water, *position* and *pressure energy*. The position or potential energy of the water is measured as a height above a selected datum. In Fig. 3.2, if we assume that level

C is the lowest relevant to the work in hand on the site, it can be assumed to be the datum. The energy of any particle of water in the pores is, therefore, measured as a height above the level C. A particle X at the level B has a position energy or potential energy of c measured in feet or perhaps in metres, since that is the height of the particle above the level C. A particle at y feet or metres below B has a position energy of $(c - y)$ feet or metres, since that is its height above C. A particle Z has zero position energy since it is at the same level as C.

The pressure energy of each of these water particles is measured by the height *above* the particle to the water table, provided there is no movement of the water. X, therefore, has zero pressure energy, Y has y feet or metres of pressure energy, and Z has c feet or metres of pressure energy. Of course, when there is no movement, as in this instance, there is no velocity energy. It is interesting to note that when the position and pressure energies of X, Y and Z are added, they each amount to c feet or metres. Thus, when there is no movement in the water, each particle has the same total energy, in situations such as that depicted in Fig. 3.2 (when the water table is horizontal). One way of showing this equivalence of energy is to insert into the soil small tubes—*piezometer tubes*—which are filled by the pressure of the pore water at each point. The height to which the water rises in the tube represents the pressure energy of the water in feet of head, and the height of the piezometer point above datum represents the position energy. Thus, a piezometer tube inserted at Y would show a level of water rising to y feet or metres above Y. A piezometer at Z would show a pressure rise in the tube of c feet or metres. Both these would bring the water level to the same elevation above C as the water table. Both particles have the same energy or *head* (which is the more usual term).

3.4. Flowing Ground Water

Quite frequently, water is flowing slowly through the soil. This movement is not visible to the eye if the water in a borehole is observed, but the amount of movement can be judged if the slope of the phreatic surface is estimated from the standing-water levels in boreholes (Fig. 3.1). The standing-water level takes some time to establish itself in equilibrium. The borehole must, therefore, be left open for a period to allow of this equilibrium to be confirmed.

As water flows through the soil, even at a very slow rate, it experiences a resistance due to the close packing of the particles. The finer the soil, the greater the resistance. This frictional resistance causes the water to lose part of its energy. Thus across a site the water may be found to possess a high energy at one point and a low energy at another, the head being gradually lost through friction in the soil. Excavation in a site of this kind may produce difficulties unless the whole situation is thoroughly understood beforehand.

The efficiency of a soil in carrying a building depends, as has been pointed out, on the intergranular pressure. Since the pore pressure plus the intergranular pressure gives the total pressure, reduction in pore pressure is one way of increasing what is rightly called the effective pressure—the pressure which exists between soil particles and which develops resistance to applied load. The aim of the foundation designer, therefore, is usually to reduce the potential and pressure energy of the pore water, and to maintain it at a low level. This gives the best conditions for the support of buildings. The function of a drain, in fact, is to reduce the two types of pressure and position energy in the pore water. The drain pipe is open to atmospheric pressure—air can flow through it. Any water in it is, therefore, at atmospheric pressure, and has no pressure energy. The drain also carries the water to the lowest level, and therefore reduces its potential energy to a low figure.

The drain is a device for reducing the energy of water by gravitational means, but if pumping, for example by well-points, is used, power is supplied to effect this reduction in energy more quickly. As the water is removed, the phreatic surface drops rapidly (Fig. 3.3). The steepness of the phreatic surface indicates a relatively rapid flow of ground water which is then removed through the wells. This has the effect of temporarily maintaining the phreatic surface at a low level to allow of excavation in the dry. The cessation of pumping, however, will result in the water rising towards its original phreatic surface. The particles of water regain their pressure energy. In such circumstances, the reinstatement of the pressure energy has, on occasion, resulted in a building being forced out of the ground because the forces exerted by the ground water had not been recognized, nor had provision against "floating" of the building been made.

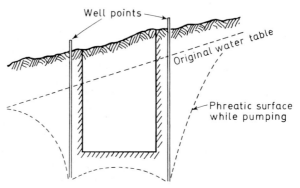

Fig. 3.3.   Control of phreatic surface.

3.5. Hydraulic Gradient

A term which must be understood if the flow of water through soils is to be studied adequately is the *hydraulic gradient.* This refers to the rate of loss of head. This loss of head or of energy of water flowing through the soil is caused by the friction of the water against the particles of the soil. The greater this resistance, the more rapidly is the energy of the water dissipated. The loss of head taking place during the passage of the water can be measured over a given distance, and this measured loss of head, divided by the distance through which the water has travelled, represents the average hydraulic gradient or loss of head per unit of distance. Distance and head are both measured in feet or metres and the hydraulic gradient is, therefore, given as a ratio. It is equivalent to the "1 in —" description of a physical gradient.

For a soil with a uniform permeability, the velocity of flow through the soil is proportional to the hydrualic gradient which causes the movement. In other words, if the hydraulic gradient is doubled, then the speed of flow of the water is also doubled. If the hydraulic gradient is cut to one-third, then the flow of water falls in velocity to a third of its previous value.

3.6. Permeability

The permeability of the soil, or the rate at which water can flow through it, is of importance in all foundation work where the water table is not absolutely horizontal. Tests on samples of soil measure the rate of flow under a given head, and the result of such tests is reported as the velocity of flow under unit hydraulic gradient. This figure is known as the *coefficient of permeability*. Since flow through the soil is laminar, each individual flow through the voids keeping to its own channel and not mixing with the others in turbulent flow, the velocity of flow is proportional to the hydraulic gradient. This relationship is known as *Darcy's Law*. It can be used to determine the rates of flow through the soil under given conditions of head. Since the coefficient of permeability is the velocity of flow under unit hydraulic gradient, it is merely necessary to multiply by the hydraulic gradient of the particular site conditions to obtain the velocity of flow through the soil. To obtain the quantity of flow, the cross-sectional area through which the flow takes place must be known. This is studied in the section on flow nets.

The range of coefficient of permeability is very large, and depends principally on the sizes of the particles in the soil. From the finest gravels down to the coarsest clays, the difference in velocity through the soil under the same hydraulic gradient may be in the ratio of millions to one. For this reason, the units used in defining the coefficient of permeability may vary. For the coarsest soils—the most permeable—units of cm/sec may be adequate. If the soil is extremely fine, then other units may be used, such as microns/sec or feet/year. A useful conversion factor is worth remembering: cm/sec multiplied by one million gives feet/year.

The range of permeabilities of soil is enormous. It can range from 4000 microns/sec for coarse sand, to one-thousandth of a micron/sec and less, for clays. The permeability of soil is very easily changed by slight variations in the density or grading of the material. Thus, one or two very accurate determinations of permeability in the laboratory are not quite as helpful as they would seem to be for the architect on the site. Some idea of the range of permeability on a site where ground-water problems occur is, however, useful.

The relationship between the three parameters, *speed*, *permeability* and *hydraulic gradient*, is explained by the relationship

Velocity = hydraulic gradient × coeff. of permeability.

This is a useful and simple relationship by which seepage and flow problems can be treated.

3.7. Flow Nets

A pictorial representation of the flow of water through soil, and of the loss of head experienced, is useful in allowing the architect to understand the changes in head velocity and effective pressure which take place in a foundation subjected to flowing ground-water conditions. This representation is usually called a *flow net*. The flow net describes the flow of the ground water by a twin series of lines. One set of lines shows the tracks of the particles of water as they flow through the soil. These are called *flow lines*. The other set of lines, which are at right angles to the flow lines, illustrate the loss of head, or the hydraulic gradient. These are called *equipotential lines*, for they join points of equal availability of head.

Some general impressions can be rapidly obtained from an inspection of the appearance of a flow net. The space between two flow lines can be looked upon as a "channel". Since the flow through the soil is not turbulent but smooth and laminar, these channels can be considered distinct from each other. An examination of such a channel shows that it may become narrower and perhaps wider again at a further point in the direction of flow. This, in turn, indicates a change in velocity. As the same quantity of water flows through all portions of the channel the velocity must increase in the narrower portions. Thus, when flow lines come close together, one can expect a higher velocity.

Similarly, the equipotential lines are spaced so that they indicate equal drops in head or losses of energy as the water flows through the soil. Since each of the lengths of flow path between successive equipotential lines suffers the same drop in head, when the equipotential lines are closer together the loss in head is more rapid in relation to distance. In other words the hydraulic gradient is greater.

The linear distances between successive equipotential lines are thus significant. In Fig. 3.4 two such distances are given as examples. The head lost between "a" and "b" is the same as that lost between "c" and "d". Since the distances travelled for the same loss of head are different, the hydraulic gradients must be different. Between "a" and "b" the hydraulic gradient is substantially less than that between "c" and "d". Equipotential lines are thus closer together where the

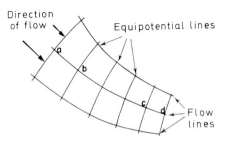

Fig. 3.4. Flow and equipotential lines.

loss in head is more rapid (*i.e.,* where the friction or resistance is greater). This underlines the fact that the velocity through the soil is proportional to the hydraulic gradient. The "meshes" or "fields" of the net become smaller and more compressed where the velocity is high and the hydraulic gradient large.

There are several methods by which flow nets for given conditions can be drawn. That which gives the greatest advantage in understanding the flow of water through soils is by sketching. This technique is by no means easy, but even a badly constructed flow net carried out by sketching gives a far greater insight into the mechanism of flow than any produced by more precise methods.

The most important features of a completed flow net are that the flow lines and equipotential lines are drawn at right angles to each other wherever they cross, and that two flow and two equipotential lines adjacent to each other always form a "square"—with curved sides! Flow always takes place between a top and a bottom flow line.

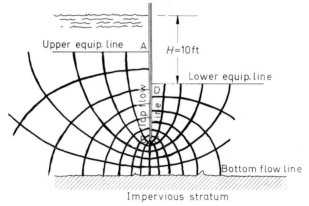

Fig. 3.5. Flow past sheet piling.

In Fig. 3.5, the top flow line is impervious and is represented by the surface of the sheet pile, the water flowing down one side, and up the other. The bottom flow line is also impervious, being the rock on which the more permeable material rests. Figure 3.6 shows how flow takes place between an impervious lower surface and a phreatic line which is the top flow line within the material.

The other two important lines which must be identified before the net can be drawn are the upper and lower equipotential lines. At any point on these lines the total head available to cause flow is constant. The head may consist of various combinations of pressure and position head. In Fig. 3.5, the upper and the lower equipotential lines show equal pressure head at all points added to equal position head. In Fig. 3.6, the upper equipotential line shows varying pressure head allied to varying position head. The lower potential is shown to be zero, for the water has been led out at the bottom of the system (zero position head) into a drainage filter which is at atmospheric pressure (zero pressure head). Where the flow lines meet the upper and lower equipotential lines, the angle of intersection must be a right angle. Similarly when the equipotential lines meet the top and bottom flow lines, the 90° direction must be maintained.

In all examples, the flow takes place between the top and bottom flow lines from the upper equipotential line to the lower. There are variations of the tracks of flow. Sometimes, in a dam for example, the top phreatic flow line is not taken to a drain, but cuts the downstream face of the dam, forming a seepage surface. When the top flow line is a phreatic surface, it is quite difficult to construct accurately, but several pointers may help in trial sketching:

(a) The top flow line must be at right angles to the equipotential lines.

(b) Since the top flow line, as a phreatic surface, has zero pressure (atmospheric) the equal drops in head represented by the ends of the equipotential lines must refer to position head only. In other words, they are spaced apart by equal vertical distances.

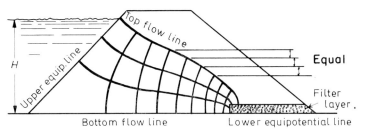

Fig. 3.6. Seepage through a dam.

3.8. *Seepage Flow*

From the finished flow net, if it is carefully and accurately drawn, it is possible to calculate the amount of water flowing through the soil. Several characteristics must be determined. First, the total loss of head must be decided; in Fig. 3.5, for example, this is represented by H, which is the difference in level between the surface of the water when it first started to flow through the soil, and the level of the water at the tail race or downstream area. Similarly in Fig. 3.6 the total loss of head is measured from the water surface to the level of the toe drain. The second figure which must be known is the permeability of the soil. This can be measured by standard techniques. The flow through the soil is equal to the velocity multiplied by the area through which the flow takes place, or

$$q = Aki$$

since the velocity is given by coefficient of permeability (k) multiplied by the hydraulic gradient (i).

However, in the examples shown in Figs. 3.5 and 3.6 and in similar problems which are often encountered in the design of foundations, the area through which the flow takes place varies. At the bottom of the sheet piling in Fig. 3.5 the area through which the water passes under the toe of the piles is small. It is very much larger as the water approaches the lower equipotential line. Similarly the hydraulic gradient (i) which is required is equal to the loss in head divided by the distance through which the water has passed. There are, however, many different lengths of flow path, and the calculation of the average hydraulic gradient for use in the formula is rendered more difficult.

On each flow passage (between two selected flow lines) we have the same number of equal drops of head, and we have along each equipotential line the same number of flow passages. In Fig. 3.5, for example, there are 15 drops of head to represent the total loss of head. There are also 6 flow passages. Thus, since the areas are "squares" there is no need to measure the exact distances or widths. Instead, the number of squares can be used in the calculation.

$$q = Aki = \text{No. of flow "squares" (M)} \times k \times \frac{H}{\text{No. of equipotential "squares" (N)}}$$

$$= kH \frac{M}{N} = kH \frac{6}{15}.$$

This gives the flow in whatever units are in use, if the flow net has been drawn correctly. Much practice is required in drawing flow nets, but the effort is worthwhile.

3.9. Seepage Pressure and Piping

As the water flows through the soil and loses head, its energy is transferred to the particles past which it flows, and a drag on these particles is set up. If this drag is in the same direction as the action of gravity, the intergranular or effective pressure becomes greater and the soil is stable. If, however, the flow takes place upwards, as in Fig. 3.5 on the right-hand side of the sheet piling, then the drag is upwards against the action of gravity, and tends to reduce the effective pressure between the particles. If this drag is sufficiently large, the effective pressure between particles will be reduced to zero, and a physical lift of the material within the excavation will take place. The danger of this occurring is greatest when the hydraulic gradient is high—when the flow net shows a close network of squares. For example, from the toe of the pile in Fig. 3.5 there are 7 squares left, out of the 15 in the whole length of the flow passage from the upper equipotential line to the lower. This means that of the total head represented by H, the head loss up to the toe of the pile is $(8/15)H$. Thus there remains $(7/15)H$ feet or metres of head to be lost between the toe of the pile and the tail-race level (C to D). The uplift pressure at C $(7/15)H\gamma_w$ thus acts as an upward drag on the particles between C and D. The downward intergranular pressure at this point is equal to the bulk density of the soil less the static pore pressure at C. The uplift pressure represented by the head lost between C and D must be less than the intergranular pressure if the particles are not to be lifted and forced to flow into the bottom of the excavation. This upward flow of sand and water is called *piping*. The factor of safety against piping is the static intergranular pressure divided by the uplift pressure due to loss of head.

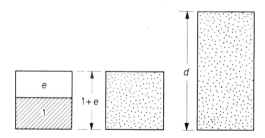

Unit base areas in all diagrams
Fig. 3.7. Critical hydraulic gradient.

If calculations from the flow net and from the known physical characteristics of the sand show that there is a danger of piping taking place, the intergranular pressure must be increased without offering resistance to the flow of water (which would produce still greater seepage pressure). The remedial measure to be taken is to lay, on the surface of the sand and within the cofferdam, a layer of heavy but very permeable material. Open-textured, large-gravel layers give the necessary extra pressure while letting water escape easily without resistance.

3.10. Critical Hydraulic Gradient

In Fig. 3.7, the total weight of the model soil sample is

$$1 \text{ ft}^3 \times G_s \gamma_w \text{ lb/ft}^3 + e \text{ ft}^3 \times \gamma_w \text{ lb/ft}^3 = \gamma_w(G_s + e) \text{ lb.}$$

This weight is resting on one square foot of area, and the total pressure is thus $\gamma_w(G_s + e)$ lb/ft^2. The pore pressure at the base is equal to the head of water above the base, and this is $\gamma_w(1 + e)$, since the water is dispersed throughout the sample.

The effective pressure is:

$$\text{Total pressure} - \text{pore pressure} = \gamma_w(G_s + e) - \gamma_w(1 + e)$$
$$= \gamma_w(G_s - 1).$$

This has been obtained by a depth of soil in the sample of $(1 + e)$ ft. Thus to obtain the effective pressure for any other depth of soil we must divide by $(1 + e)$ and multiply by the required depth.

For a depth d (third diagram) the effective pressure is:

$$\frac{\gamma_w(G_s - 1)}{1 + e} d$$

and this must be greater than the pressure applied by the head lost through the distance d. If this head is h, the pressure is $h\gamma_w$. When there is equality we have the critical condition and piping is imminent:

$$h\gamma_w = \gamma_w \frac{(G_s - 1)d}{1 + e} \quad \text{or} \quad \frac{h}{d} = \frac{G_s - 1}{1 + e}.$$

Thus the critical hydraulic gradient is $(G_s-1)/1+e$. If there is so much resistance to flow that this value is exceeded, piping will occur.

COMPUTATION PANELS THREE

Prerequisite reading: Chapter 3 and Sections 2.5, 2.6, 2.7

Reminders
See reminders for Computation Panels Two
Coefficient of permeability: k (length/time)
Rate of flow: q (length^3/time)
Hydraulic gradient: i (ratio)
Cross-sectional area of soil through which flow takes place: A (length^2)
Darcy's law: $v = ki$
$$q = Aki$$
Critical hydraulic gradient: $= \dfrac{G_s - 1}{1 + e}$

Seepage force per unit of volume: $i\, \gamma_w$ (load/length^3).

CP3A

PROBLEM: To determine the coefficient of permeability from the results of a laboratory test

Data
    Water is allowed to flow through 30 cm of sand (6 cm diameter) under a constant head of 60 cm. In one minute 800 g of water flowed through.

Result required
    Coefficient of permeability.

Method of attack
    (1) By Darcy's law the velocity of flow is proportional to the hydraulic gradient. When the water enters the sand it has an energy represented by 60 cm head. When it leaves, the energy is zero. The distance travelled while this energy is dissipated is 15 cm. The hydraulic gradient is therefore 60 in 15 or 4 in 1 or 4 cm/cm. The hydraulic gradient is a ratio.

(2) The rate of flow is 800 g/min = 800 ml/min. The area through which this flows is 6 cm diameter.

$$\pi r^2 = 9\pi \text{ cm}^2.$$

The velocity of flow is thus $800/9\pi$ cm/min. (One ml is taken to be the same as one cm^3.)

(3) By Darcy's law $v = ki$ or $k = v/i = (800/9\pi) \times \frac{1}{4} = (200/9\pi)$ = 28·3 cm/min which is the coefficient of permeability.

CP3B

PROBLEM: To define the pressure exerted at various depths in a stratum of soil

Data

A site investigation gives the following figures:
(A) Surface to 4 ft depth; coarse dry sand ($\gamma_d = 115$ lb/ft^3).
(B) 4 ft to 8 ft; fine saturated sand ($\gamma = 125$ lb/ft^3).
(C) 8 ft to 15 ft; saturated clay ($\gamma = 117$ lb/ft^3).

e for coarse sand = 0·5; e for fine sand = 0·6;
e for clay = 0·9; Water table is at 4 ft depth.

Results required

(a) Total pressure at 7 and 14 ft depth.
(b) Pore pressure at 12 ft depth.
(c) Effective pressure at 9 ft depth.

Method of attack

(1) The values of void ratio which were determined in the site investigation are not needed in calculations for pressure. Sketch the conditions.

(2) Total pressure is concerned only with bulk density. At 7 ft depth the total weight is 4 ft × 115 lb/ft^3) (A) together with 3 ft × 125 lb/ft^3 (B) or 460 + 375 = 835 lb/ft^2.

Similarly, for 14 ft depth, total pressure is 4 ft of (A), 4 ft of (B) and 6 ft of (C) or 4 × 115 + 4 × 125 + 6 × 117 = 1662 lb/ft^2 total pressure.

Table CP3C

Lowering of W.T.	Total pressure (lb/ft²)	Pore pressure (lb/ft²)	Effective (lb/ft²)	Change (%)
B	Before*	$1 \times 128 = 128$	Zero	128	−16
	After	$1 \times 107 = 107$	Zero	107	
C	Before	$4 \times 128 = 512$	$3 \times 62 \cdot 4 = 187$	325	+32
	After	$4 \times 107 = 428$	Zero	428	
D	Before	$5 \times 128 = 640$	$4 \times 62 \cdot 4 = 250$	390	+43
	After*	$4 \times 107 + 1 \times 128$ $= 556$	Zero	556	
E	Before	$12 \times 128 = 1536$	$11 \times 62 \cdot 4 = 686$	850	+19
	After	$4 \times 107 + 8 \times 128$ $= 1452$	$7 \times 62 \cdot 4 = 437$	1015	

* Capillary fringe is saturated and applies its load as an effective pressure because of zero pore pressure at the water table.

CP3D

PROBLEM: To estimate the depth to which excavation can be made in clay without risk of heave of the bottom of the excavation

Data

Excavation is in saturated clay; $\gamma = 112$ lb/ft².

An aquifer occurs at a depth of 40 ft below the surface.

A borehole establishes the piezometric head at the top of the aquifer as 45 ft.

Result required

The depth to which excavation may be safely carried.

Method of attack

(1) Make a sketch of the conditions (Fig. CP3D).

(2) The head which would start flow at the bottom of the excavation is the difference between the piezometric level (which is artesian) and the level of the bottom. This is $45 - D$ ft. or $(45 - D)\gamma_w$ lb/ft².

(3) The clay is saturated so the effective pressure of the particles of clay at the top of the aquifer is the total weight less the pore

pressure. The total weight is γD. The pore pressure is the weight of water in the soil between the bottom of the excavation and the top of the aquifer $(\gamma_w D)$.

$$\begin{aligned} \text{Effective pressure} &= \gamma D - \gamma_w D \\ &= (112 - 62\cdot4)\, D \\ &= 49\cdot6\, D \text{ lb/ft}^2. \end{aligned}$$

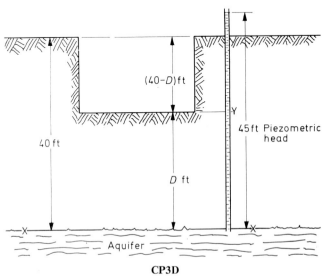

CP3D

(4) When this downward effective pressure at the top of the aquifer is exceeded by the drag or seepage pressure caused by flow of water into the bottom of the excavation (to be pumped away) a dangerous situation develops. The apparent weight of the soil particles becomes zero as the seepage pressure overcomes the effective or intergranular pressure. Heaving of the bottom occurs.

(5) The seepage pressure is equal to the density of water multiplied by the hydraulic gradient. The average hydraulic gradient in the soil through which flow takes place is the head lost divided by the thickness D. The head in the bottom of the excavation is atmospheric or zero. Thus the head lost is represented by the height of water in the piezometer tube above Y, the level of the bottom of the excavation. This is $(45 - D)$ feet.

(6) The hydraulic gradient, therefore, is $(45-D)/D$ and the seepage force on every cubic foot of the soil where this hydraulic gradient is applicable (the depth D) is $(45-D)\gamma_w/D$. Multiplying by the number of cubic feet (assuming a column of soil 1 ft^2 in area) the seepage pressure per square foot is $(45-D)\gamma_w$. Equating this to the effective pressure for the critical condition,

$$(45-D)\gamma_w = 49\cdot6\gamma \quad \text{or} \quad D = 25 \text{ ft (where } \gamma = 112 \text{ lb/ft}^3).$$

Thus the greatest depth to which the excavation can be taken is $(40-D)$ ft or 15 ft.

                                                                    CP3E

PROBLEM: To determine the rate of seepage under a cofferdam and its factor of safety against piping

Data

    Coefficient of permeability, $3\cdot9 \times 10^{-3}$ cm/sec.
    $G_s = 2\cdot70$, $e = 0\cdot74$.
    Head retained by the piling, 22 ft.
    Near piling at downstream boundary, the flow net has an average dimension (for each equipotential drop) of 3·7 ft.
    The flow net has 16 equipotential drops and 5 flow channels.

Results required

    (a) The quantity of seepage under the sheet piling for each foot of length.
    (b) The factor of safety against piping.

Method of attack

    (1) The amount of seepage is found by obtaining first the velocity of seepage flow. This, according to Darcy's law, is equal to the coefficient of permeability multiplied by the hydraulic gradient. In this problem, if a "square" of the flow net is taken to represent unity, then the hydraulic gradient is head/number of equipotential drops, or 22 ft/16 drops. The velocity of flow (assuming units are, later, equated) is 22 ft/16 drops $\times$ $3\cdot9 \times 10^{-3}$ cm/sec.

(2) The quantity of seepage is the velocity multiplied by the cross-sectional area through which the flow takes place. Since the distance over which the head is lost was measured, above, in terms of "squares" or equipotential drops, the area (1 ft at right angles to the paper, multiplied by the width of the flow channel) can be given as 5 flow squares.

The quantity is thus (in mixed units)

$$= \frac{22 \text{ ft}}{16} \times 3\text{·}9 \times 10^{-3} \text{ cm/sec} \times 5.$$

(3) The units must be equated. If we choose feet and seconds, it is necessary only to replace centimetres by the equivalent 0·0328 ft/cm.

Thus

$$q = \frac{22}{16} \times 3\text{·}9 \times 10^{-3} \times 0\text{·}0328 \times 5$$

$$= \frac{140712}{16} \times 10^{-7}$$

$$= 0\text{·}00088 \text{ ft}^3/\text{sec.}$$

(4) The factor of safety against piping is obtained by comparing the hydraulic gradient at the danger area—the downstream boundary of the piling—with the critical hydraulic gradient.

The loss of head in each square is the same; the squares represent equipotential drops. The total head lost is 22 ft and there are 16 equipotential drops.

The loss of head is thus 22/16 feet per "square" or 1·37 ft. This occurs over the average dimension of one "square" (3·7 ft) on the downstream face of the piling and the hydraulic gradient is therefore 1·37/3·7 or 0·37.

(5) The critical hydraulic gradient for this soil is

$$\frac{G_s - 1}{1 + e} = \frac{2\text{·}7 - 1}{1 + 0\text{·}74} = \frac{1\text{·}70}{1\text{·}74} = 0\text{·}98.$$

If the hydraulic gradient is less than 0·98 no piping will occur. In this foundation, the factor of safety against piping is 0·98/0·37 or 2·6, which is quite adequate to ensure that the excavation planned can be carried out.

PROBLEM: To determine the uplift pore pressure below a basement floor when the water table is horizontal and there is no flow of water through the soil

Data

The horizontal floor of a basement lies at 20 ft below ground level.

The water table is horizontal and is 5 ft below ground level.

There is a horizontal rock surface at an average depth of 23 ft below the bottom of the basement; otherwise the soil is uniform (Fig. CP3F).

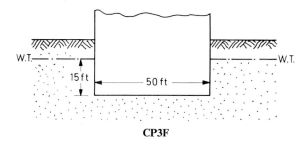

CP3F

Results required

Diagram of uplift pore pressure over the underside of the base-ment.

Method of attack

(1) It is assumed that the basement has been constructed for some time so that conditions have attained equilibrium.

(2) Since the water table is horizontal, no head is lost between one side of the building and the other for there is no excess head to cause flow through the soil.

(3) The pore pressure at a depth of 15 ft below the water table is

$$15 \times 62 \cdot 4 = 936 \text{ lb/ft}^2.$$

This acts across the whole of the base of the slab and applies a uniformly distributed load of 936 lb/ft^2 over 50 ft^2, or (936 × 50)/2240 (about 21) tons on each foot of length of the building at right angles to the paper.

Results required

(a) Graph showing the equilibrium moisture content to a depth of 20 ft when the water table is 4 ft below the surface.

(b) Similar graph for the conditions with a water table lowered to 7 ft below the surface.

Method of attack

(1) Draw Fig. CP3H/1 so that any value of void ratio can be read off when the effective stress is known.

(2) Decide in general terms what the effective stress is at various depths below the surface.

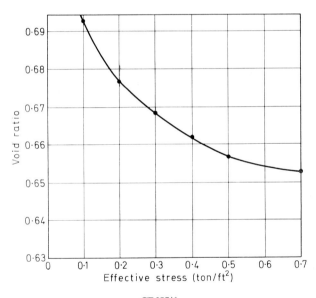

CP3H/1

Effective stress = Total stress due to bulk density less pore pressure.

$$= \gamma h - \gamma_w(h - H)$$

where H is the depth of the water below the surface. When h is less than H, the pore pressure is added to the total pressure because it is, in fact, a suction as is explained in the text.

$$\sigma' = \gamma h - \gamma_w(h - H)$$
$$= 122\,h - 62{\cdot}4\,(h-4)$$
$$= 59{\cdot}6\,h + 249{\cdot}6\ \text{lb/ft}^2$$

for the 4-ft deep water table

$$\text{or} = 0{\cdot}0266\,h + 0{\cdot}111\ \text{ton/ft}^2.$$

(3) Draw up Table CP3H/1. Column (2) is obtained from the equation in the last section and e is then read off, for column 3, from Fig. CP3H/1.

Table CP3H/1

(1) h (ft)	(2) Effective stress (ton/ft²)	(3) e from Fig. CP3H/1	(4) $m = \dfrac{e}{G_s}$ (%)
0	0·111	0·692	25·2
5	0·244	0·673	24·5
10	0·377	0·664	24·2
15	0·510	0·657	23·9
20	0·634	0·653	23·8
		Mean: 0·668	

(4) It is now necessary to make a check to ensure that the bulk density, on the value of which the resulting moisture content depends, is close to that assumed. In this instance, the average void ratio is 0·668.

$$\text{Bulk density} = \frac{G_s + e}{1 + e}\gamma_w$$

$$= \frac{2{\cdot}75 + 0{\cdot}668}{1{\cdot}668} \times 62{\cdot}4 = 128\ \text{lb/ft}^3.$$

(5) This last figure indicates that the estimate of bulk density has been too low—122 instead of 128 lb/ft³. Trying again with 128 lb/ft³ we have Table CP3H/2 based on:

$$\text{Effective stress} = 128\,h - 62{\cdot}4\,(h-4)$$
$$= 0{\cdot}0292\,h + 0{\cdot}111\ \text{ton/ft}^2.$$

Table CP3H/2

(1) h (ft)	(2) Effective stress (ton/ft²)	(3) e from Fig. CP3H/1	(4) $m = \dfrac{e}{G_s}$ (%)
0	0·111	0·692	25·2
5	0·257	0·672	24·4
10	0·403	0·663	24·1
15	0·549	0·656	23·8
20	0·595	0·654	23·8
		Mean: 0·667	

With a mean void ratio of 0·667, the bulk density is found to be 127 lb/ft³. This is close to 128 lb/ft³ but, in fact, a comparison of column 4 in the two tables shows that the refinement of a second trial was unnecessary.

(6) The same procedure is followed for a depth of water table of 7 ft.

$$\text{Effective stress} = 128\,h - 62\cdot4\,(h-7)$$
$$= 0\cdot0266\,h + 0\cdot195 \text{ ton/ft}^2.$$

Table CP3H/3 gives the final results.

Table CP3H/3

(1) h (ft)	(2) Effective stress (ton/ft²)	(3) e from Fig. CP3H/1	(4) $m = \dfrac{e}{G_s}$ (%)
0	0·195	0·678	24·6
5	0·328	0·667	24·2
10	0·461	0·659	24·0
15	0·594	0·654	23·8
20	0·718	0·652	23·7
		Mean: 0·662	

(7) It is now only necessary to draw the diagrams required—Fig. CP3H/2—from columns (1) and (4) of the last two tables.

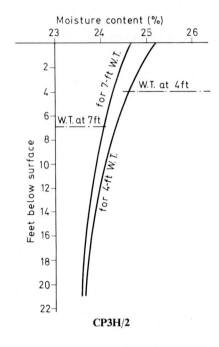

CP3H/2

PART II

Chapter 4

Stress in a Loaded Soil

4.1. Nett Loading Intensity

When a site is first visited, it is assumed that the soil is in equilibrium under its own weight, and that there are no violent changes in soil conditions, such as rapid fluctuation of the level of the water table. Excavation, and the subsequent application of load from a building, will alter these conditions. This chapter is concerned with the extra stresses imposed by the presence of the building after it is completed. There are additional stresses already in existence under the natural state of the ground. If, by excavation or other means, some of the natural stress in the soil is relieved, this stress may be reintroduced by part of the weight of the building before the calculation of the excess stress is commenced. In difficult ground, where the capacity of the soil to carry load is low, the technique of removing some of the original soil in order to reduce the original stresses in the foundation material, before the building is commenced, is one which allows of construction in conditions where the imposition of a heavy excess pressure would be impossible. The additional loading on a plane in the ground due to the load imposed by the building is called the *nett loading intensity*, and it is for this extra loading that the foundations must be designed. The nett loading intensity is reduced by any relief given by removal of the existing soil, as, for example, for basements. The nett loading intensity is reported in terms of pressure (lb/ft^2; ton/ft^2; kg/cm^2, etc.).

4.2. Contact Pressure

The load is transmitted to the ground through a foundation structure which, in itself, has a certain amount of stiffness. This makes the transfer of the nett loading intensity a little more complex than is apparent at first sight. If, for example, an extreme condition were taken, and the foundation structure assumed to be a simple polythene sheet of zero stiffness, then a uniformly distributed loading applied to the sheet would be transferred to the ground as a uniformly distributed contact pressure.

If the same uniformly distributed pressure is applied to a stiff foundation—a concrete footing—this rigidity causes the contact pressure to change, from the uniform load applied by the building to the footing, to a non-uniform distribution. This non-uniform distribution, acting as a contact pressure under a stiff raft, footing or pad, is high at the edges of the footing and lower in the centre. If the footing is infinitely stiff, the pressure at the edges is theoretically infinite. These need cause little concern, for it merely means that the clay flows a little to adjust itself. The intensity is then redistributed and becomes something which is nearer to a uniform pressure. It is still, however, lower in the centre and higher at the edges.

It would be quite unrealistic to try to develop means of taking into account this variation in intensity of loading for small footings, and in this chapter only uniform contact pressures are used. In view of the other discrepancies and approximations inherent in considering stresses in such a material as soil, this further approximation to a uniform contact pressure is unlikely to lead to dangerous error for buildings.

4.3. Theoretical Analysis of Stress

For each application of a nett intensity of loading to the soil in the form of a concentrated or uniform contact pressure, the problem is to determine the stresses which are brought into play in the soil. These are then compared with the strength of the soil as discussed in Chapter 5. In order to be able to calculate from mathematical theory the values of the imposed stresses within the soil, it is necessary to assume certain basic conditions for the state of the soil if any progress is to be made. Unless these assumed conditions are simple ones, the calculation of stresses within a mass of soil becomes very complex. The conditions assumed before the calculation commences are usually:

(a) The soil is homogeneous.

(b) The soil has the same properties in all directions (*i.e.,* it is isotropic).

(c) The soil continues to a great depth to be exactly as it is at the surface.

(d) The soil continues to extend unchanged in all directions ((c) and (d) together are usually written as the condition that the soil mass is *semi-infinite*).

(e) The soil displays elastic properties (it returns to its original shape when the stress is withdrawn).

These conditions are so manifestly at variance with the known properties of the materials we find on an actual site that it would seem to be almost a waste of effort to calculate stresses in the soil from the assumptions listed. Attempts have been made, reasonably successfully, to study more complex arrangements. Two- and three-layer systems, each layer having different properties, have been calculated, but the complex results obtained have not had much direct application, and the simpler attack is all that is recommended for the architect.

This chapter contains three reference tables from which the extra stress applied at various points in the soil can be calculated. It must be realized that these figures are not "exact". In view of the unsound assumptions made, this is not surprising. The figure calculated, however, can be used as a guide to the conditions obtaining. Great exactitude of calculation is, therefore, not required. The error involved in assuming the soil to be homogeneous, isotropic, semi-infinite and elastic is sufficient to neutralise any exact figures obtained from elaborate formulae.

The chief value of the derivations described in this chapter is first, in showing how great a mass of soil is likely to be involved in the stress complex, and secondly, in giving at least an approximate guide to the order of magnitude of the stresses operating in the soil. Quick sketches of stress contours can readily pin-point levels or positions where there is likely to be a build-up of stress due, perhaps, to overlapping effects of footings in close proximity. In these regions particular care must be taken in the design of the foundations.

The tables treat the simpler types of footing usually adopted in buildings, and the stress studied is the vertical excess stress on horizontal planes caused by the nett intensity of loading from a simple footing. Other, more elaborate, foundation conditions and other types of stress, *e.g.,* shear, can be dealt with in a similar manner. Tables dealing with these can be found in the more exhaustive treatises on soil mechanics. They would be confusing in an introductory volume.

4.4. Influence Factors

The tables have been constructed from the results of the basic mathematics of Boussinesq (first performed in 1885) so that any size of footing can be studied. For each case a dimensionless factor—the ratio of one linear dimension to another—is calculated, and the tables used to extract an *influence factor*. This is a figure which, when multiplied by the applied nett intensity of loading, allows estimation of the required stress in the soil.

From the tables, by extracting values of induced stress at various points, it is possible to build up a graphical representation of the contours of stress within the soil. This is a method and technique which is illustrative and worth the effort required. It is usual to consider, for such graphical representations, a two-dimensional cross-section of a long strip footing.

4.5. Stresses caused by a Concentrated Load

Although it is unlikely that many foundation structures in a building will apply a concentrated load, for it can be approximated only by a stanchion applying load through a very small pad, it represents the basic loading from which all the other tables have been developed. In Fig. 4.1 the concentrated load on the surface is represented by P, the depth by z and the distance from the line of the load, radially and horizontally to the point at which the stress is required, by r. Boussinesq calculated, from the conditions listed above, the stresses which would result at the point X. The stress we are interested in is the vertical pressure on a horizontal plane passing through that point. This can be calculated by means of the Table 4A. In a particular problem calculate the ratio of the radius to the depth (r/z) from the conditions of the problem, and enter Table 4A with this number to obtain the influence factor. This value is then multiplied by the value of the nett loading intensity (P) and divided by the square of the depth (z^2). This is the only table where the multiplica-

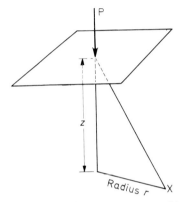

Fig. 4.1. Stress due to a concentrated load.

Table 4A

Influence factors for a concentrated load

Ratio $\dfrac{r}{z}$	Influence factor K	Ratio $\dfrac{r}{z}$	Influence factor K	Ratio $\dfrac{r}{z}$	Influence factor K
0·00	0·478	1·24	0·047	1·90	0·011
0·08	0·470	1·30	0·040	2·00	0·009
0·10	0·466	1·36	0·035	2·10	0·007
0·20	0·433	1·40	0·032	2·20	0·006
0·40	0·329	1·46	0·028	2·30	0·005
0·60	0·221	1·50	0·025	2·40	0·004
0·80	0·139	1·56	0·022	2·50	0·003
1·00	0·084	1·60	0·020	2·60	0·003
1·10	0·066	1·66	0·018	2·70	0·002
1·14	0·060	1·70	0·016	2·80	0·002
1·20	0·051	1·80	0·013	3·00	0·002

Multiply the influence factor (K) by the load P and divide by z^2 to obtain the vertical pressure at a depth z and at a radial distance r from the line of action of P.

tion of the influence factor by the nett loading intensity does not give
the stress directly. This stems from the use of a concentrated load in
this first example.

The result is the vertical stress at the point X induced by the
application of a concentrated load P at the surface. This vertical
stress is additional to any stress already in action due to the original
conditions of the site, and illustrates the result of the additional
loading only.

4.6. Stresses caused by a Uniformly Distributed Strip Load

A strip footing is a common type of foundation structure and
gives a two-dimensional problem. We do not need to look at a
perspective or solid view of the conditions of loading, but merely to
cut off a slice and observe it from the end. The distances required are
all measured on the same plane at right angles to the length of the
strip footing. Table 4B gives the vertical pressures under the centre
of the strip footing and also at points horizontally distant from the
centre by lengths equal to $\frac{1}{4}$, $\frac{1}{2}$, $\frac{3}{4}$ and the whole width of the footing.

Table 4B

Influence factors for a strip load

$\dfrac{B}{z}$	K for $\dfrac{x}{B}$ equal to				
	Zero	$\frac{1}{4}$	$\frac{1}{2}$	$\frac{3}{4}$	1·0
	1·000	1·000	0·500	0·000	0·000
4·00	0·959	0·902	0·497	0·089	0·019
2·00	0·818	0·735	0·480	0·214	0·075
1·00	0·550	0·510	0·409	0·288	0·185
0·80	0·462	0·437	0·370	0·285	0·205
0·50	0·306	0·298	0·275	0·242	0·205
0·40	0·248	0·244	0·231	0·212	0·188
0·25	0·158	0·156	0·153	0·147	0·140
0·20	0·127	0·126	0·124	0·122	0·117

Multiply the influence factor (K) by the uniform pressure on the strip footing to
obtain the vertical pressure at a depth z and at a lateral distance x from the
centre of the strip.

These figures allow of curves being drawn to show the variation of vertical pressure under the strip footing over a horizontal distance of up to twice the width of the footing (Fig. 4.2).

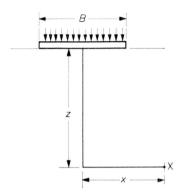

Fig. 4.2. Stress due to a uniformly distributed strip load.

4.7. Stresses caused by a Uniformly Distributed Load on a Rectangular Area

Many footings for stanchions are of a square or rectangular shape. The determination of stresses at various depths under such a footing can be carried out by obtaining influence factors for the stress

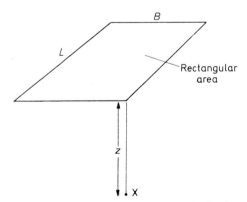

Fig. 4.3. Stress under corner of rectangular footing.

Table 4C

Influence factors for a loaded rectangular area. L/z

$\dfrac{B}{z}$	0·1	0·2	0·3	0·4	0·5	0·6	0·8	1·0	1·6	2·0	3·0	4·0
0·1	·0047	·0092	·0132	·0168	·0198	·0222	·0258	·0279	·0306	·0311	·0315	·0316
0·2	·0092	·0179	·0259	·0328	·0387	·0435	·0504	·0547	·0599	·0610	·0618	·0619
0·3	·0132	·0259	·0374	·0474	·0559	·0629	·0731	·0794	·0871	·0887	·0898	·0901
0·4	·0618	·0328	·0474	·0602	·0711	·0801	·0931	·1013	·1114	·1134	·1150	·1153
0·5	·0198	·0387	·0559	·0711	·0840	·0947	·1103	·1202	·1324	·1350	·1368	·1372
0·6	·0222	·0435	·0629	·0801	·0947	·1069	·1247	·1361	·1503	·1533	·1555	·1560
0·8	·0258	·0504	·0731	·0931	·1104	·1247	·1461	·1598	·1774	·1812	·1841	·1847
1·0	·0279	·0547	·0794	·1013	·1202	·1361	·1598	·1752	·1955	·1999	·2034	·2042
1·6	·0306	·0599	·0871	·1114	·1324	·1503	·1774	·1955	·2203	·2261	·2309	·2320
2·0	·0311	·0610	·0887	·1134	·1350	·1533	·1812	·1999	·2261	·2325	·2378	·2391
3·0	·0315	·0618	·0898	·1150	·1368	·1555	·1841	·2034	·2309	·2378	·2439	·2455
4·0	·0316	·0619	·0901	·1153	·1372	·1560	·1847	·2042	·2320	·2391	·2455	·2473

Multiply the influence factor (K) by the uniform pressure on the rectangular footing to obtain the vertical pressure at a depth z under the *corner* of the footing.

under a corner of the area. Table 4C gives some of these influence
factors for various proportions of breadth to depth and length. The
table refers to the vertical stress at a point immediately below one
corner of a uniformly loaded rectangular footing (Fig. 4.3).

If the footing or raft is more complex it is necessary only to
imagine it composed of a number of rectangles. To find stresses at
points such as X in Fig. 4.4 the stresses under the corners of A, B, C
and D need only be added together to give an indication of the

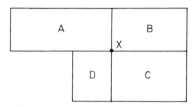

Fig. 4.4.   Stress under irregular area.

vertical stress at some depth below X. This, of course, can be considered as only approximate, but the characteristics of the material
found on a site do not agree with those ideal properties assumed in
the mathematical derivation.

4.8. Influence Charts

The use of the tables of influence factors can be tedious especially
when the stress is required at many points, or when the footing which
is applying the load is not a simple geometrical shape. Speeding up
of the task can be achieved by drawing graphs from the figures given
in the tables. If these graphs are drawn to a large scale, the influence
factors can be read off easily for any value of r/z, B/z, etc. It is suggested that such graphs should be drawn out. They are useful when
the problems of later chapters have to be solved. The readings from a
well-drawn graph are sufficiently accurate, and should not be looked
upon as approximate. The assumptions made of homogeneity,
isotropy and semi-infinity for the soil are likely to introduce more
errors than even a sketchily drawn graph.

The most useful and most generally applicable method of determining stresses in the soil, for the architect who wishes to understand more fully how foundations behave, and why cracks appear, is the use of *influence charts*. These have been very cleverly designed by Professor N. M. Newmark of the University of Illinois. They give, in graphical form, the influence factors for stress and vertical displacement in elastic materials (which is what we assume our soil to be) at all levels below the surface.

The chart in which we are interested defines the vertical stress on horizontal planes produced by any surface loading. A small reproduction of this chart is shown in Fig. 4.5. It is used as follows:

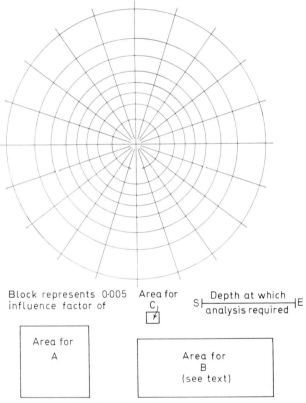

Block represents 0·005
influence factor of

Area for
C

Depth at which
S├────────────┤E
analysis required

Area for
A

Area for
B
(see text)

Fig. 4.5. Newmark's influence chart.

(a) Decide on the depth at which the stress is to be evaluated. The line SE at the bottom right-hand corner of the chart then represents this depth to scale.

(b) Draw a plan of the footing *to the scale defined in* (a).

Examples are given in Fig. 4.5:

A is a 15-ft square footing when SE represents 20 ft, the depth at which the stress is required.

B represents a rectangular area of 105 ft × 23 ft when SE represents 35 ft. depth to the stressed level.

C is a 10-ft square footing when the depth for the analysis is 80 ft.

(c) Lay the drawing of the footing, prepared on tracing paper, on the influence chart. The point vertically below which the stress is required is placed at the centre of the diagram. If the stress is required below the centre of the footing, the centre of the plan is placed over the centre of the chart. If the stress is required under a corner, the corner of the scale drawing of the footing is placed over the centre of the chart. The chart is drawn symmetrically, so that the scale drawing can be swung round on the centre point of the chart without affecting the result.

(d) Count the number of blocks or spaces covered by the scale drawing, taking account of portions of blocks cut by the edge of the scale drawing of the footing.

(e) Multiply the number of blocks or spaces covered (whatever their size they each count as one) by the influence factor given on the diagram. This gives the proportion of the applied contact pressure which appears as a vertical stress at the level and position selected. If, for example, the scale drawing of a footing covered 76·3 spaces, and the influence factor given on the chart was 0·001, then the stress at the level chosen would be 0·076 of the applied loading. If the loading were 2 ton/ft² the stress at the depth selected would be 0·152 ton/ft². ("Ton" refers throughout to a "long ton".)

4.9. *Bulb of Pressure*

What is almost as important as the value of the stress at a given point below a footing is the mental picture which the architect holds of how these stresses range in value with depth and with the horizontal distance from the loaded area. To be able to make such a mental assessment of the mass of soil affected by the superimposed loading is of great value on the site, especially where soft and compressible layers have been discovered by the site exploration. By remembering how the stresses vary in value, the architect can estimate whether the founding of a footing at a lower or a higher level, or with a greater or less nett intensity of pressure, would best serve the stability of his construction. In this section, students should use graph paper and draw out the lines showing contours of equal pressure.

When the distribution of pressure is drawn out, it can be seen that there is a certain volume of soil within which stresses are relatively high, and further volumes, lying outside the first, where the stresses are lower. The outer line enclosing the *bulb of pressure* or volume of soil particularly affected can be arbitrarily chosen. It can represent say one-tenth or one-fifth of the nett intensity of loading applied to the site. Within this bulb lies the soil which must be carefully examined by site exploration before it is stressed. A glance at any bulb of pressure shows that there is little use in examining only the soil near the surface unless it is known that the stratum is really homogeneous to some depth. In fact, the wider the footing used, the greater must the exploration extend in depth. For an isolated footing the diagrams, such as Fig. CP4D, indicate that soil is stressed up to 40 % of the applied pressure to a depth of one-and-a-half times the width of the footing. If a building is carried on a rigid raft, or if the individual footings are set close together so that the effects of their bulbs of pressure overlap, the depth to be explored may be very much greater than might at first glance be thought to be necessary.

Figure CP4D shows that the lines of equal pressure (isobars) indicate higher stresses close to the surface and lower stresses at greater depths. This is in accordance with diagrams which show how pressure varies at the centre of a strip footing as the depth increases. In the Computation Panels such variation is calculated numerically. However, when clays are normally consolidated they usually show greater strength as the depth increases, because the weight of the soil drives out the water and achieves consolidation of the clay. This decrease of strength as the surface is approached is the opposite of what is required, for the greatest applied stresses are near the surface.

Thus, as depth increases in a normally consolidated soil, the applied stress decreases and the strength increases. The loading must be such that at any point the safety of the foundation is assured, and the strength offering a greater resistance than the stress applied.

Bulbs of pressure can also be drawn for other types of stress in the soil. For shear stresses under a strip load, for example, the isobars are actually portions of circles. It is sometimes of value to draw out the isobars of shear, but the nett value of the increase in vertical pressure allows of the calculation to proceed on sound lines in order to achieve a suitable design of foundation.

COMPUTATION PANELS FOUR

Prerequisite reading: Chapter 4

CP4A

PROBLEM: To determine the decay of vertical pressure laterally from the line of a vertical concentrated load

Data

A load of 2 tons is applied vertically on the surface of the soil, and can be considered to be concentrated over a very small area. The soil may be considered homogeneous, isotropic and semi-infinite.

Result required

A diagram showing the variation in vertical pressure in the soil at a depth of 5 ft.

Method of attack

(1) Decide on values of radius r (Fig. 4.1) to be used and draw up Table CP4A.

(2) Values of r/z are obtained by dividing r by the depth 5 ft.

(3) Calculate z^2 which in this instance is 25 ft².

(4) Multiply 2 tons by K (Table 4A) for each point chosen and complete column 4.

(5) Divide by the value of z^2 and draw Fig. CP4A.

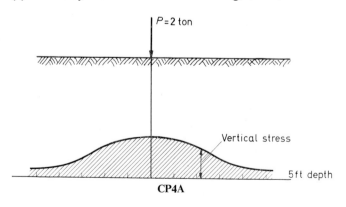

CP4A

Table CP4A

r (ft)	$\dfrac{r}{z}$	K (from Table 4A)	KP	$\dfrac{KP}{z^2}$ (ton/ft²)	$\dfrac{KP}{z^2}$ (lb/ft²)
0·0	0·0	0·478	0·956	0·038	86
2·0	0·4	0·329	0·758	0·030	68
3·0	0·6	0·221	0·442	0·018	40
5·0	1·0	0·084	0·168	0·007	15
7·0	1·4	0·032	0·064	0·003	6
10·0	2·0	0·009	0·018	0·001	2
14·0	2·4	0·004	0·008	0·000	0

CP4B

PROBLEM: To determine the decay of vertical pressure with depth under a concentrated load

Data

As for CP4A, 2 tons rests on the surface, concentrated over a small area (Table 4A).

Result required

Diagram showing values of pressure under the load at different depths.

Method of attack

(1) Decide on values of depth to be chosen. These should be close together when the values are small and further apart at deeper depths.

Table CP4B

z (ft)	z^2 (ft²)	$\dfrac{0\cdot4775}{z^2}$	Vertical pressure (ton/ft²)
0·1	0·01	47·8	95·6
0·2	0·04	11·9	23·8
0·3	0·09	5·3	10·6
0·4	0·16	3·0	6·0
0·8	0·64	0·75	1·50
1·2	1·44	0·3	0·60
2·0	4·00	0·1	0·20

(2) Construct Table CP4B as in problem CP4A, but this time r is zero and the value of the vertical pressure in the soil is 0·4775 divided by the square of the depth, multiplied by the load, 2 tons.

(3) Draw Fig. CP4B.

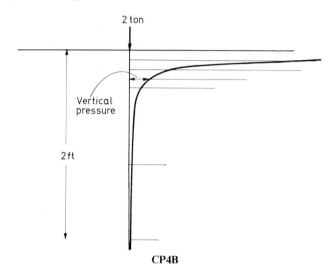

2 ton

Vertical
pressure

2 ft

CP4B

CP4C

PROBLEM: To trace the decay of stress laterally from the centre of a strip load

Data

A strip load is 3 ft wide and carries a uniformly distributed load of 2 ton/ft^2 at the surface (Table 4B).

Results required

(a) Vertical pressures on horizontal plane at 3 ft depth.
(b) Vertical pressures on horizontal plane at 6 ft depth.

Method of attack

(1) Draw up Table CP4C giving the ratios x/B.

(2) $z = 3$ ft; $B = 3$ ft. Thus $\dfrac{B}{z} = 1\cdot 0$.

(3) $z = 6$ ft; $B = 3$ ft. Thus $\dfrac{B}{z} = 0\cdot5$.

(4) To find the vertical pressure, multiply the influence factor by q, which is the same for both depths (2 ton/ft^2).

Table CP4C

$\dfrac{x}{B}$ for both depths	x (ft)		Influence factor K (Table 4B)		Vertical pressure (ton/ft²) : $q \times$ I.F.	
	for 3 ft	for 6 ft	$\dfrac{B}{z} = 1\cdot0$	$\dfrac{B}{z} = 0\cdot5$	at 3 ft	at 6 ft
Zero	Zero	Zero	0·550	0·306	1·10	0·61
$\frac{1}{4}$	$\frac{3}{4}$	$\frac{3}{2}$	0·510	0·298	1·02	0·59
$\frac{1}{2}$	$\frac{3}{2}$	3·0	0·409	0·275	0·82	0·55
$\frac{3}{4}$	$\frac{9}{4}$	$\frac{9}{2}$	0·288	0·242	0·58	0·48
1·0	3·0	6·0	0·185	0·205	0·37	0·41

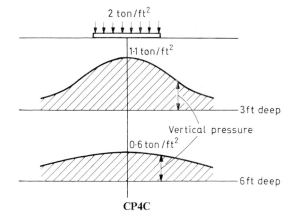

CP4C

CP4D

PROBLEM: To draw bulbs of pressure under a uniformly loaded strip footing

Data

The strip footing is 4 ft wide and carries a uniformly distributed load of 1·5 ton/ft² (q).

Results required

Bulbs of pressure (composed of isobars of vertical stress in the soil) for values of 0·5, 0·4 and 0·2 q (0·75, 0·60, 0·30 ton/ft²).

Method of attack

(1) The vertical pressure at any point is equal to the influence factor from Table 4B multiplied by the applied loading (q).

(2) The influence factor, for the particular vertical pressure chosen, equals the pressure chosen, divided by q. A vertical pressure in the soil of 0·2 q is found where the influence factor is 0·2.

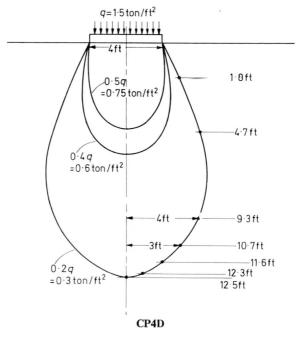

CP4D

(3) In Table 4B pick out values of B/z where K (the influence factor) is 0·20. These lie, for example, between 0·25 and 0·40 (B/z) for $x/B = \frac{1}{4}$ and between 2·00 and 4·00, and between 0·25 and 0·40 for $x/B = \frac{3}{4}$.

(4) Draw up Table CP4D by finding, by proportion, where the value of B/z lies for all values of $K = 0·20$ in Table 4B.

(5) Find the value of z by dividing the breadth of the footing by the values of B/z.

(6) Plot points from the data x and z in the table, x being measured outward from the centre line of the footing, and z being measured downwards from the surface. These points form the bulb of pressure (Fig. CP4D).

Table CP4D

x	0	1	2	3	3	4	4	feet from centre
x/B	0	$\frac{1}{4}$	$\frac{1}{2}$	$\frac{3}{4}$	$\frac{3}{4}$	1	1	
B/z	0·32	0·33	0·35	0·37	2·22	0·43	0·85	for
z	12·5	12·3	11·6	10·7	1·8	9·3	4·7 ft	$K = 0·20$
B/z	0·68	0·72	0·95		for			
z	5·9	5·6	4·2 ft		$K = 0·4$			
B/z	0·89	0·97	4·00		for			
z	4·5	4·1	1·0		$K = 0·5$			

PROBLEM: To determine the decay of intensity of pressure with depth under a square footing

Data
   The footing is 12 ft square, and carries a load of 2 ton/ft^2.

Result required
   A diagram showing variation of pressure under the centre of the footing as depth increases.

Method of attack
   (1) Divide the footing into four squares, each of 6 ft side.
   (2) Consider the pressure under one corner of one of these squares.
   (3) Multiply this value by four to obtain the approximate pressure under the centre of the footing, since four corners meet at that point. Use Table 4C.
   (4) Draw the diagram (Fig. CP4E) from the figures in Table CP4E.

Table CP4E

Value of B = L = 6 ft

z (ft)	$\dfrac{B}{z}$ and $\dfrac{L}{z}$	K (from Table 4C)	Vertical pressure $= 2 \times 4 \times K$ (ton/ft^2)
60·0	0·1	0·0047	0·04
12·0	0·5	0·0840	0·67
6·0	1·0	0·1752	1·40
3·8	1·6	0·2203	1·76
3·0	2·0	0·2325	1·86
2·0	3·0	0·2439	1·95
0·6	10·0	0·2498	2·00

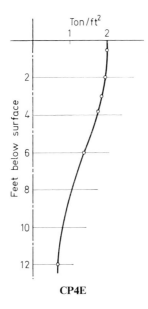

CP4E

CP4F

PROBLEM: To compare stresses in soil under a building as obtained from tables of influence factors and from Newmark's chart

Data

A building stands on a raft of the shape shown in Fig. CP4F. The soil is assumed to have the properties described in this chapter, and the building stands on the surface.

Results required

(a) The vertical pressure under X and Y at 15 ft below the surface using Table 4C.

(b) The vertical pressure under X and Y at 15 ft below the surface, using Newmark's chart.

Method of attack

(1) The shape of the building must be drawn to the scale defined by SE = 15 ft (Fig. 4.5). The lengths concerned are 7·5, 10·5, 15 and 21 feet. There is no need to make even slide rule calculations for this conversion. The lengths required for the dimensions of the scale drawing of the raft can be obtained graphically.

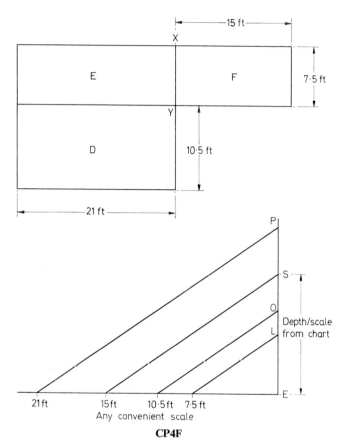

CP4F

(2) First draw on a horizontal line, to any convenient scale, the lengths concerned. Then at right angles set off the exact length of SE as taken from the chart to be used. Join the point S to the point H which is 15 ft on the scale chosen. Lines parallel to SH will mark off lengths EL, EO and EP which are the lengths to be used to represent 7·5, 10·5 and 21·0 feet in the drawing of the plan of the raft (Fig. CP4F).

(3) Place the drawing, made on tracing paper, over the chart, first with the point X at the centre of the chart and then with the point Y at the centre. For each position count the number of blocks enclosed within the plan of the raft. Multiply these by the influence value for one block.

(4) Using the chart in the way described, the following results were obtained:

X at centre of chart: 64 blocks covered: 0·005 per block.

Y at centre of chart: 81 blocks covered: 0·005 per block.

Multiplying, we have the condition that, at 15 feet below the raft, the vertical stress is 0·32 times the loading pressure directly under X. Similarly, directly under Y, the vertical stress at 15 ft depth is 0·41 times the pressure applied at the surface by the raft.

(5) In using Table 4C to determine the stress under the point Y, the stress under a corner of rectangle F, and the stress under the corners of rectangles D and E, are all added together. Table CP4F/1 gives the necessary calculations:

Table CP4F/1

$(z = 15 \, ft)$

Rectangle	Length (ft)	Breadth (ft)	L/15	B/15	Influence factor (Table 4C)
D	21·0	10·5	1·4	0·7	0·16
E	21·0	7·5	1·4	0·5	0·13
F	15·0	7·5	1·0	0·5	0·12
					Total 0·41

which agrees with the value from the chart.

(6) In considering the point X only two rectangles need be studied. These are rectangle F and the combined rectangles D and E. Table CP4F/2 gives results which agree with the result from the chart.

Table CP4F/2

Rectangle (ft)	Length (ft)	Breadth (ft)	*L*/15	*B*/15	Influence factor (Table 4C)
G (D + E)	21·0	18·0	1·4	1·2	0·20
F	15·0	7·5	1·0	0·5	0·12
					Total 0·32

out at different normal pressures on a clay soil without giving time for the water to be squeezed out and the pore pressure to be dissipated, then it makes little difference what normal pressure is applied. In all the tests, the shear strength of the soil will apparently be the same (DF, Fig. 5.2).

If, however, time is given for the water to be expelled and for the particles to come closer together, then the graph GK (Fig. 5.2) is obtained, showing that even clay soils increase in strength as the normal pressure is increased, provided that pressure is the effective or intergranular pressure. To obtain such a line as GK (Fig. 5.2) it is necessary to arrange that the test specimen should remain for some time under the normal pressure which is to be used during the test so that the pore pressure can be dissipated and the load carried as an effective pressure.

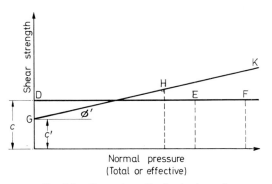

Fig. 5.2. Shear strength of cohesive soil.

If, however, time is not available for this, it is possible to carry out the shear tests under a measured total pressure, while the pore pressure is measured instrumentally at each loading. This measurement of pressure enables the effective pressure at each stage to be determined by subtracting the measured pore pressure from the total pressure applied. Thus, for a cohesive soil, at least two important values of the shear strength can be obtained

In Fig. 5.2 there are two lines DF and GK which give values of the shearing resistance of the same soil. The difference between these is important. The line DF is at a constant height c above the zero line. The value c is known as the *cohesion* which is the term for a shearing strength when no normal pressure is applied. A handful of dry sand has no cohesion and falls apart into its constituent particles. A handful of clay, on the other hand, remains intact because it retains its particles in position by cohesion. When such a clay is loaded quickly, and the pore pressure is not dissipated, the shearing resistance offered is the same as if the clay were unloaded. No matter under what pressure the water lies, it has no shear strength, and if the normal load applied is carried merely by pressure in the water-filled voids, no extra strength is gained. The result is the line AB. Unlike sands, clay can be overtaken and failed in shear by being rapidly loaded. The strength of a granular sub-soil increases with the loading applied (Fig. 5.1) but the increase of loading on clay must be very slow to achieve a similar effect because of the slow rate of egress of the pore water.

On the other hand, if time is given for the particles to come closer together and for the water (which has no shear strength) to leave the soil, the clay shows a development of shear strength in relation to effective pressure which approximates to that of a granular soil. The cohesion (or strength with no normal pressure) still remains but it is less than in the *immediate* or *rapid test*. The increase of shear strength with normal pressure is represented by the *angle of shearing resistance* (ϕ') (related to effective pressure). The important relationship of shear strength to normal pressure can be written as a formula, usually known as Coulomb's equation:

$$s = c' + \sigma' \tan \phi'.$$

This is merely a shorthand method of saying that shear is equal to cohesion plus the normal stress times the tangent of the angle of shearing resistance. All these factors can be determined by standard tests.

5.4. *Methods of Shear Testing*

It is an assumption made in this volume that the architect will not, normally, carry out tests himself. He will not possess a soil mechanics laboratory or employ the technicians to operate it. Occasionally, however, in reading the report of a site investigation, the architect must be familiar with the principles behind the methods of test, since these are often quoted in support of the values presented. The significance of the figures quoted often relates to how they were obtained. In the study of the shear strength results given by the site exploration the methods used to obtain the values are worth considering.

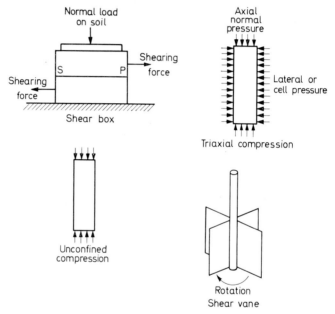

Fig. 5.3.   Methods of testing for shear strength.

There are four principal ways in which shear strength can be measured, and each of these has its peculiar advantages and applications. The most obvious method is to take a block of soil, insert it into two bottomless boxes and pull the one across the other until the soil shears along the plane SP (Fig. 5.3). This is a direct method and gives points such as A, B and C in Fig. 5.1. Samples of the soil are loaded by different normal loads, and the stresses, both normal and shear, calculated from the area of the box. A line is drawn between the points obtained. This test can be carried out for clays to obtain the *immediate shear* value such as is shown by DEF in Fig. 5.2. If each normal load is allowed to remain in position until consolidation of the sample takes place, the shear characteristics related to effective stress can also be determined by the shear box (GHK).

An important method of measuring shear strength is known by the title of *triaxial compression*. In this method, the sample of soil is prepared in the form of a small cylinder and is inserted into an appara-tus in which a lateral water pressure can be applied to all sides of the sample while it is being loaded in compression (Fig. 5.3). When the sample fails there are two values of stress from which shear strength can be determined. These are the *lateral or cell pressure* and the *axial or normal pressure*. If these two values are set off along the axis of normal pressure (the horizontal axis in Figs. 5.1 and 5.2), a semicircle can be drawn through them (L and P, for example in Fig. 5.4). Similarly, other semicircles can be drawn for other values of

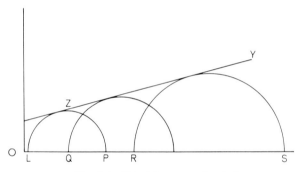

Fig. 5.4.   Triaxial compression tests.

lateral pressure and axial pressure (*e.g.*, R and S). When a number of such semicircles have been drawn, the line ZY which most nearly touches them all defines the shear characteristics. The reason why these semicircles can be used in this way depends on mathematical arguments on how material behaves under stress. It is not necessary that the architect should understand this in detail, but the proofs can be found in any text-book on strength of materials or soil mechanics.

When a pure clay is tested in triaxial compression, and no time is given for the effective stress to be developed, the immediate shear strength is the cohesion, and all the circles are of the same diameter (Fig. 5.5). For a clay without any granular material in its composition, only one of these circles need really be determined. In Fig. 5.4 the points L, Q and R, which are at the left-hand side of the semicircles, represent the lateral or cell pressures. Thus if, in Fig. 5.5, the semicircle TU is chosen, there need be no lateral pressure at all, since T is on the zero line. This makes the apparatus much less complex, and the test reduces to one of simple compression which is relatively easy to carry out (Fig. 5.3). The value of the axial compressive stress which causes failure is represented by the position of the letter U (Fig. 5.5), and the shear strength can thus be obtained simply by dividing the compressive strength by two, since the height of the horizontal line WM above the base is equal to the radius of the circle.

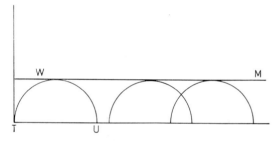

Fig. 5.5. Triaxial and unconfined compression tests on clay.

This *unconfined compression* test is viable only with pure clays the immediate strength of which is represented by such lines as WM or DEF. However, as such soils present some of the most difficult problems, the unconfined compression test gives valuable information. A glance at Figs. 5.1 and 5.4 shows that it would not be applicable for a granular soil showing an angle of shearing resistance, nor would it apply to a clay soil where the pore pressure has been dissipated and the effective stress allowed to come into action.

A useful method of determining the shear strength *in situ* even at the bottom of a bore hole is by means of the *shear vane*. A vane consisting of four wings of thin metal is pushed into the soil and then rotated. The torque required to twist the vane in the soil gives a measure of the shear strength of the soil over the surface of the cylinder swept out. A small vane can be used in the laboratory, but the advantage of this test is its ability to measure shear strength before the soil is removed in a so-called "undisturbed" sample.

Of the tests described in this section, the architect will find the last two most useful. He can certainly carry out the vane test himself, for example in trial pits, and there is little difficulty in the pure compression test in *unconfined compression*. The triaxial test is much more complicated and much more costly, but must be resorted to if the soil is likely to have an angle of shearing resistance.

5.5. Summary of Shear Strength

From this portion of the chapter it is clear that there is no such thing as a unique value of shear strength for a soil. Its strength depends on how it is loaded. A lateral cell pressure of OR in Fig. 5.4 develops a compressive strength in the soil of OS, whereas a lateral pressure of OL develops a failing strength of only OP. Similarly, the shear strength measured by the height to the line ZY is greater in the first instance.

For granular soils, since water is easily expelled from them, the total stress is also the effective stress. For pure clays there are two chief conditions in which shear strength must be found. The one is the *immediate shear strength* when the *cohesion* (c) is measured before water has had a chance to be expelled under the weight of the normal load, and the shearing resistance remains the same whatever the loading. This is known as the "$\phi = 0$" condition (lines DEF and WM). The other condition is when the clay has been allowed to consolidate before its strength is measured. This allows the pore pressure to be dissipated and the intergranular or effective pressure to come into play. The *angle of shearing resistance* now has a value greater than zero (ϕ') and the cohesion will probably be somewhat smaller (c'). Note that when the shear test is carried out with respect to effective rather than total normal pressure, the parameters are marked by a prime—c' instead of c and ϕ' instead of ϕ.

The unconfined compression test is a simple and useful one for pure clays. For such soils the elaborate triaxial-compression form of testing gives little more information than the simpler test. It is more effective to use the money available for site investigation and testing in pure clays for a large number of simple tests rather than for a small number of elaborate tests for shear.

The immediate test is usually of more value to the architect than any other. He usually erects a building in a time which is very short compared with that required to dissipate pore pressure in a deep stratum of clay. The strength of the clay will be the same at the end of construction as at the beginning. Over a longer period the strength of the clay under the consolidation caused by the weight of the building will begin to follow line GHK of Fig. 5.2. This fact can be looked upon as an assurance that if the building can be erected on clay without a shear failure, then it will continue to be safe, for the strength will increase.

If, however, the structure takes years to build—say a great cathedral—the architect requires to know something about the possible increase in strength as time goes on, and wants to have figures on which to base his foundation design. This necessitates a full triaxial-compression investigation to obtain the line GHK (Fig. 5.2). When it is known what increase in shear strength is to be expected in time to come, then it may be possible to effect economies by using a lower factor of safety during construction. The ultimate factor of safety as the structure ultimately reaches completion will be greater, the difference being represented by the gap between lines DEF and GHK. With the values of c (in a $\phi = 0$ condition) and the values of c' and ϕ' for the clay, an intelligent design for the foundations of a large structure can be carried out. The guidance of specialists in soil mechanics should be obtained for important steps of this kind.

5.6. Nature of Compressibility

If the soil is highly compressible, and this is the type of soil of which the architect wishes to be forewarned, the ultimate change in volume when a load is applied does not occur for some considerable time after the loading has been completed. On the other hand, if the soil is of a granular type it is not highly compressible and usually completes its change in volume when the load is applied. Such soils offer few problems of consolidation and settlement. They make excellent foundations if they are contained and also maintained at a constant moisture content or with a reasonably constant level of the water table. They show an increase in strength with increasing pressure, and little settlement is experienced. This section, therefore, concerns itself only with soils of fine-grain structure and high void ratio—the cohesive soils. These are the soils which present problems of compressibility.

The major change in volume which occurs when such soils are loaded with the weight of a building is due to a reduction in void ratio or to a reduction of the volume of voids in the material. In a saturated clay soil this can occur only if the water is gradually expelled. The reverse can take place; water can be taken up by clay also, and expansion can take place. In some circumstances this phenomenon can cause problems in foundation stability. It is not the purpose of this book, however, to study the problems of osmotic pressure or any of the more delicate physical properties of clays which control such movements. The problem of compression is, however, studied, for it leads to an even more significant problem to the architect, that of settlement.

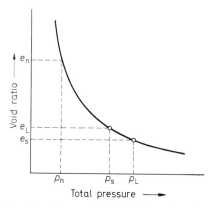

Fig. 5.6. Compressibility and consolidation.

For each soil studied and tested in the laboratory, it is essential to have a figure which represents the degree to which the soil can be compressed under a given loading. Just as the permeability of the soil is measured by means of a coefficient representing the velocity of the water through the soil under a unit hydraulic gradient, compressibility is measured by a coefficient which gives the *decrease in unit volume per unit increase in pressure*. This is called the *coefficient of compressibility*, (m_v). The decrease in volume suffered by a cohesive soil is, in fact, the decrease in voids within that soil, and consequently can be expressed as a decrease in the void ratio. It is thus possible to draw a graph (such as that in Fig. 5.6) showing how the void ratio for a particular soil decreases as the pressure increases.

A good deal of information about the behaviour of clays in foundations can be obtained by loading the clay, unloading it and reloading. The process can be followed in Fig. 5.7. First, the soil,

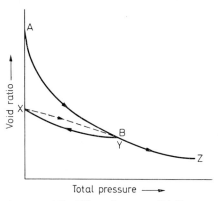

Fig. 5.7. Effect of preconsolidation.

assumed to have been free from excess loading previously, shows a decrease of void ratio with an increase of pressure, at the rate illustrated by the curve AB. Then, when the load is released, a certain amount of swelling takes place, but the clay does not recover to the extent of its original volume. As the load is decreased, the void ratio increases slightly, along the line BX (the solid line). When load is applied for the second time, the void ratio decreases once more, usually along a line such as the dotted XB. When the point Y is reached, the line is back on its original track, and continues down towards Z with increasing pressure. The line ABYZ is called the *virgin consolidation curve*, for it illustrates the behaviour of clays which have not previously been compressed.

The curve XBYZ, which has a distinct change in direction in the B–Y area, represents the behaviour, under compression, of clay which has previously been loaded to some extent. This change in direction is useful in determining the previous history of a clay. If the soil shows, on test, a change of void ratio with loading such as XBYZ, the inference is that it has been already loaded. In geological times, for example, clays were compressed under great depths of ice or under layers of sediment which have since been eroded away. Clays which are from more recent geological times may never have had such precompression, and are thus more likely to show settlement than the *overconsolidated* clays of the older measures. It is possible, from the diagrams obtained from tests, to determine at least approximately the pressure to which the clays have been subjected, but this is of somewhat academic interest to the architect working on the foundations for a particular building. It is, however, useful to study the geological history of an area, for such knowledge at least gives indications of the kind of compressibility—ABZ or XBZ—likely to be encountered.

5.7. Calculation of Coefficient of Compressibility

The techniques by which clay is tested in order to discover its coefficient of compressibility are not of vital importance to the practising architect who is unlikely to have the necessary equipment for carrying out the tests, or the staff to operate the laboratory. He must, however, understand what is meant by the figures he receives, and how the compressibility measured in the laboratory can be used in the calculation of settlement of a building founded on the clay tested.

Figure 5.8 shows, in diagrammatic form, what happens when pressure is applied to a cohesive soil, and time is allowed to elapse so that water is driven out of the voids. The voids then become smaller in total volume and the solid particles more closely packed. In the model soil sample, the solid particles are assumed to be packed together with no voids, so that they remain as a solid mass of a constant unit volume. This model soil sample, as described in Chapter 2, is again an appropriate means of understanding the changes involved. Figure 5.8 shows diagrammatically a soil sample under a small pressure p_s, and possessing a large void ratio e_L. The total volume of the soil sample is thus $(1+e_L)$, the voids being assumed saturated with water. This condition under the small pressure p_s is unchanging and is assumed to be in equilibrium.

Now if the pressure is changed from a small pressure p_s to a larger pressure p_L, the void ratio decreases as is shown by the two circled points on the curve in Fig. 5.6. The void ratio, after conditions have settled into equilibrium, is e_s, and the total volume of the sample is $(1+e_s)$. We thus have the decrease in volume equal to the difference between the volumes of the voids:

$$\text{Volume change} = e_L - e_s.$$

The increase in pressure is, similarly, the difference between the larger and smaller pressures:

$$\text{Change in pressure} = p_L - p_s.$$

The decrease in volume of this sample per unit increase in pressure is, therefore,

$$\frac{e_L - e_s}{p_L - p_s}.$$

But the sample is originally of a volume $(1+e_L)$. Thus the decrease in volume for a unit increase in pressure for every unit in volume is obtained by dividing by the original volume.

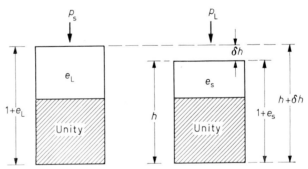

Fig. 5.8.   Effect of pressure on compressible soil.

The *coefficient of compressibility*, which is the *decrease in unit volume per unit increase in pressure*, is

$$m_v = \frac{e_L - e_s}{p_L - p_s} \frac{1}{1 + e_L}.$$

The units represented by this formula are the inverse of a pressure (in^2/ton or cm^2/kg) but there is no need to try to visualize what this means. If the units are used correctly, they look after themselves.

5.8. Variation of Coefficient of Compressibility with Pressure

The coefficient of compressibility is not a fundamental property of the clay. It depends on the pressure which has already been applied, and on the void ratio so produced. Fig. 5.9 is an enlarged portion of the consolidation curve of Fig. 5.6. It shows that the expression

$$\frac{e_L - e_s}{p_L - p_s} \left(= \frac{A}{B} \right)$$

is represented by the tangent of the slope of the consolidation curve. The coefficient of compressibility is, therefore, proportional to this slope. The steeper the slope, the greater the value of the coefficient.

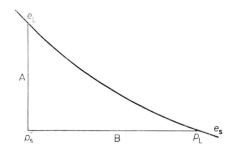

Fig. 5.9.   Calculation of coefficient of compressibility.

Thus in Fig. 5.6 it is clear that the coefficient of compressibility is higher at the lower pressures, because the slope of the curve is steeper. At the higher pressure, the slope has flattened off, and the coefficient is, therefore, smaller in value. Thus if the soil has not been compressed much previously it will have a large change in void ratio for a small increase in pressure; it will have a high coefficient of compressibility. If it has already been compressed previously, the change in void ratio for the same change in pressure is much smaller, as can be seen by the slope of the curve, and the coefficient of compressibility is also smaller. This, once more, shows how valuable it is for the architect to know the geological history of the site, for, if the clay is already overconsolidated, a different behaviour and a different value of the coefficient can be expected from those obtaining for virgin clays, or normally consolidated clays which have settled under no more than their own weight. Foundation designs in areas of over-consolidated clay will not be universally applicable in areas where only normally consolidated material is found.

5.9. Compressibility of Remoulded Clays

Clays, formed in geological times by settlement of very small particles through water, build up a very complex structure. This structure is supported only partially by direct physical contact of particles, and in some clays there is no such contact, the particles being entirely separated from each other. The intricate mesh of particles is kept in position often by electrostatic forces, and by various complex pressures within the material. If such a complex formation is disturbed or broken, it can be well understood that the skeleton structure can disintegrate and the strength of the original composition seriously decrease. Similarly there will be a consider-able difference in the behaviour under compression of clays before and after remoulding.

If two samples of the clay are taken, one quite undisturbed and the other remoulded by hand before being formed into a test sample the void ratio in the remoulded sample will be found to decrease rapidly on the A–B part of the curve, and will generally, at any pres-sure, be considerably lower than the void ratio for the same pressure in the undisturbed state. This is understandable, for once the delicate structure is broken up, the particles move more closely together in a less ordered fashion. The rate of decrease of void ratio with pressure at higher loads is probably less for remoulded samples than for the original clay. Samples of clay from overconsolidated strata may well show very little difference in behaviour, in this respect, between the undisturbed and the remoulded samples. The original structure has already been disturbed by the early consolidation by sediments or ice sheets, and the release of this pressure has caused only a very small reorientation of the particles (Fig. 5.7).

5.10. Rate of Consolidation

It is possible, by the use of the coefficient of compressibility, and the value of the extra stress applied to the soil, to determine the total compression or consolidation of the soil which will eventually take place. For a thick layer of soil, the period taken over this final consolidation is a long one. The rate of consolidation is not uniform, but is most rapid to begin with when the load is originally applied, and the architect finds his interest in the total amount of ultimate settlement of his building taking second place in his thoughts to the settlement which will take place in the first few years of the life of the structure. This may well amount to 50 or 60% of the total, the rest taking place very slowly over a much longer period.

The determination of what time will be necessary for 50 or 60% of the total consolidation to take place is a technique of some value. To determine the *rate of consolidation* is a much more complex problem than that of finding the value of the final consolidation which will take place at some unknown date in the future.

The variables, the influence of which on each other determines the rate of consolidation, can be divided into two groups:

(a) *Values relating to the clay being compressed*

k — coefficient of permeability   (length/time)

m_v — coefficient of compressibility   (length^2/load)

γ_w — density of water   (load/length^3)

(b) *Values relating to site conditions*

U_v — degree of consolidation, or the proportion of the final settlement in which interest is concentrated (often 50% or 60%; 0·5 or 0·6).

d — length of the drainage path, or the longest distance water must travel through the clay to reach a drainage layer, such as a sand or gravel stratum.

The object of the investigator, using these figures, is to determine the time taken by the consolidating layer to reach the chosen degree of consolidation.

One of the difficulties encountered in the simplification of this complex problem is that the coefficient of compressibility varies in value with the pressure applied (Fig. CP5D). By combining the first two variables and the density of water, however, it is possible to use a single factor which is reasonably constant for a given clay. This is the *coefficient of consolidation*:

$$c_v = \frac{k}{m_v \gamma_w} \text{ (length}^2/\text{time)}.$$

The other two variables dealing with site conditions are linked by the mathematical theory of consolidation, which need not concern the architect. It is sufficient to say that a quantity, called the *time factor* (T_v), has been determined, relating the *degree of consolidation* with the conditions causing consolidation. For the simple case of uniform pressure distribution, the degree of consolidation and the time factor are related by the equation

$$U_v = 1 \cdot 13 \sqrt{T_v}.$$

This does not alter with the material of the foundation and is, therefore, drawn out in Fig. 5.10. For any degree of consolidation chosen, the time factor can be read off. It should be noted that this relationship holds true only up to a degree of consolidation of about 0·5 to 0·6 (50% to 60%) of the final consolidation ever likely to be reached. This, however, is the degree of consolidation which is reached relatively quickly. If damage is to be suffered by a building through settlement, it will occur during this earlier period, after which settlement is much slower.

From the value of T_v read off from Fig. 5.10, the time taken for the chosen consolidation to occur is found by the relationship

$$t = \frac{T_v d^2}{c_v}.$$

The values of T_v and d can be obtained, respectively, from Fig. 5.10 and from the conditions on the site. The value of c_v comes from the characteristics of the clay layer the behaviour of which is under investigation.

It is not necessary to calculate c_v from the coefficients of permeability and compressibility. It can be obtained by compressing a sample of the clay and observing the rate at which this sample compresses and also what final consolidation is reached. The sample must be thin, for it is clear from the formula for t that the time taken to reach a given degree of consolidation varies as the square of the thickness. Thick samples, therefore, take a long time to reach consolidation, and for this reason cannot be used in laboratory experiments.

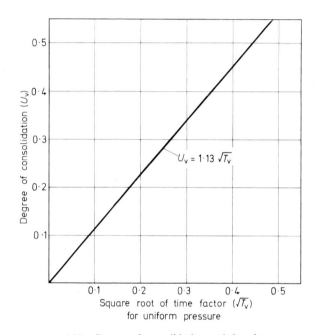

Fig. 5.10. Degree of consolidation and time factor.

By combining the formulae for U_v and t a further relationship can be worked out:

$$c_v = \frac{d^2 U_v{}^2}{1 \cdot 28\ t}.$$

If c_v is constant for the clay in question, as it can be assumed to be, then for a given value of d, the length of the drainage path, U_v is proportional to the square root of the time taken to reach that value of consolidation. The sample of clay is compressed under a chosen pressure, and the value of the times taken to reach given degrees of consolidation are recorded. From this, the value of c_v for the material is determined. The determination of the consolidation of a clay layer on a site is then merely a matter of the application of the formula for t for various values of T_v, and for the value

$$t = \frac{T_v d^2}{c_v}.$$

of the length of the drainage path. If drainage is both upwards and downwards to granular strata, the drainage path is one-half of the thickness of the clay stratum.

(3) On the other hand, the value of the intercept on the vertical axis, which defines the cohesion, is still in pounds, and must be transformed to a stress. The area of the material sheared by the box is $6 \times 6 = 36$ cm^2. Replacing cm by its equivalent in inches, 36 cm^2 is equal to $36 \left(\dfrac{\text{inch}}{2 \cdot 54}\right)^2 = \dfrac{36}{2 \cdot 54^2}$ in^2 = 5·57 in^2.

(4) Dividing the value of 54 lb, shown where the shear line intercepts the vertical axis, by 5·57 we obtain the cohesion, or shear stress at zero normal load, which is 9·7 lb/in^2.

CP5D

PROBLEM: To determine the coefficient of compressibility at various normal pressures

Data

The sample of soil was loaded in increments up to 8·5 kg/cm^2 and the load then released to zero. The decrease in thickness during loading and the expansion on release of load were measured. The sample was found to be 1·79 cm thick at the end of the test. The moisture content at the end of the test was found to be 0·253 and the specific gravity of particles was 2·75. The test results were:

Pressure (kg/cm^2)	0	0·12	0·50	2·12	8·52	0
Change in thickness (cm)	−0·011	−0·038	−0·072	−0·132	+0·118	

Result required

A table and a graph showing the variation of the coefficient of compressibility with change in total pressure.

Method of attack

(1) The soil is saturated and thus the void ratio at the end of the test can be obtained from the moisture content, for (in saturated soils) $e = mG_s$. Thus the void ratio at zero pressure at the end of the test, when the sample was 1·79 cm thick, is

$$e_s = 0 \cdot 253 \times 2 \cdot 75 = 0 \cdot 697.$$

(2) Figure 5·8 shows a model soil sample before and after being compressed. The original void ratio e_L becomes e_s and both the height and the volume of voids suffer changes indicated by the Greek letter delta. If the cross-sectional area of the sample remains unaltered during compression, then the change in volume of voids and the change in height can be compared:

$$\frac{\delta e}{1 + e} = \frac{\delta h}{h}; \qquad \delta e = \frac{1 + e}{h} \delta h.$$

In the conditions given by the test, since e is 0·697 and h is 1·79 cm., the relationship is

$$\delta e = \frac{1·697}{1·79} \delta h = 0·95 \, \delta h.$$

Thus, for every change in thickness of the sample, the void ratio changes by 95% of the numerical change in thickness. This is true even although void ratio is measured as a ratio and thickness is measured in terms of length.

(3) Using the relationship worked out above, multiply the figures in column 3 of Table CP5D by 0·95 to obtain column 4.

(4) Now fill in 0·697 at the foot of column 5, since that is the only value of void ratio we know. Work up column 5 obtaining values of void ratio after each of the increments of load. This is done by subtracting or adding the values of change in void ratio of column 4. The final figure at the top of column 5 shows the void ratio at the commencement of the test when it was not possible to determine the moisture content. Checks could, of course, have been made on another sample of the soil and the moisture content would have been equal to e/G_s or 0·831/2·75. The difference between this and other moisture contents (which can be obtained, in the same way, for other points in column 4) shows how much water has been driven out.

(5) Column 6 shows the ratio of the change in void ratio to the change in pressure for each increment of pressure.

(6) Column 7 gives the mean void ratio for each increment of pressure.

(7) Column 9 shows the values of the mean coefficient of compressibility and column 10 the mean pressure over the given ranges. Finally Fig. CP5D is drawn from columns 9 and 10.

Table CP5D

(1) p (kg/cm²)	(2) δb Change in pressure	(3) δh Change in thickness (cm)	(4) $\delta e = 0.95\delta h$ Change in void ratio	(5) e Void ratio	(6) $\delta e/\delta p$	(7) $\bar{e}$ Mean void ratio	(8) $1 + \bar{e}$	(9) m_v (6)/(8) (cm²/kg)	(10) Mean pressure p (kg/cm²)
0				0·831					
	0·88	−0·011	−0·010		0·011	0·826	1·826	0·062	0·06
0·12				0·821					
	0·38	−0·040	−0·038		0·099	0·802	1·802	0·055	0·31
0·50				0·783					
	1·62	−0·076	−0·072		0·045	0·747	1·747	0·026	1·31
2·12				0·711					
	6·40	−0·139	−0·132		0·021	0·645	1·645	0·013	5·32
8·52				0·579					
	8·52	+0·125	+0·118						
0				0·697					

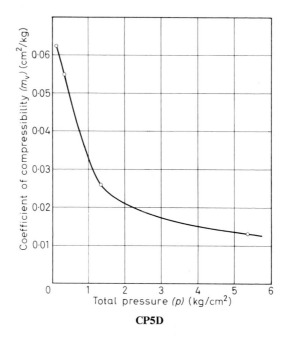

CP5D

PROBLEM: To determine the coefficient of consolidation of a sample of clay from the results of the consolidation test

Data

A sample of clay was tested in consolidation under a constant pressure. It was compressed from a thickness of one inch to a thickness of 0·950 inch before movement ceased. During the progress of the consolidation the following thicknesses were measured:

At time (t) from the start of the test (minutes)	Decrease in thickness from the original thickness (inch)
4	0·008
16	0·015
36	0·023
64	0·030
100	0·035

Chapter 6

Exploration of the Site

6.1. Geophysical Methods

So that this chapter can claim to give at least a brief summary of the methods employed in exploring a site, it is well that geophysical methods should be mentioned. They take the form of the measurement of physical properties of the soil such as electrical resistance and the rate of travel of shock waves through the soil. Changes in subsurface conditions are accompanied by changes in the properties measured, and skilled observers can correlate the measured changes with the probable differences existing below ground level. The alteration in electrical resistivity as electrodes driven into the ground are moved to wider and wider spacings gives indications of the presence and location of denser strata. Seismic methods, in which small charges of gelignite are exploded and the rate of travel of the resulting shock waves measured, is another method which has not only been successful in exploration for oil, but has shown good results over the smaller areas concerned in civil engineering construction. The method of studying the refraction of the artificially-produced seismic waves is suitable for obtaining the general geological conditions over, say, a residential area of an industrial estate, and these methods might be used more in such conditions. Geophysical methods, however, do not give the detailed information required for individual buildings, and much more precise methods are required to obtain the kind of values described in the previous chapters.

6.2. Objectives of Site Investigation

The same methods cannot be applied in every site exploration. The methods used vary, depending on the type of construction envisaged, the type of strata likely to be encountered and the nature

129

of the tests which have been specified by the architect. This last point is very important. The architect, if he is to be fully in charge of the type and nature of the foundations finally built, must be in control of the investigation carried out. Too many architects delegate this vital matter either to their structural consultants or to a professional firm of soil mechanics specialists. They should not be surprised if the results they obtain are not as helpful as they had imagined such an investigation would be. Even if the architect keeps the control of the investigation in his own hands, he must instruct the firm carrying out the work, and specify exactly what is required, as he does for the structure of the building. To ask for "a site investigation" is not only inefficient, but gives too little assistance to the investigators in their decisions on the techniques to be employed, and leaves them to guess at the information required. It also leads very often to unnecessarily costly site explorations.

The ultimate objective of the site investigation is to allow of an estimation of the allowable bearing pressure on the foundations and of the likely settlement to be encountered (Chapters 7, 8 and 9). These objectives are reached through the determination of various properties of the soil and of conditions imposed by the presence of the building (Chapters 2, 3 and 5). The immediate task of the site exploration, therefore, is to obtain these values and properties. They should be obtained in such a way that the assumption can be made with some confidence that the properties and conditions measured are those which will be found to be operative *in situ* in the soil when excavation has been carried out to the depths specified.

The architect must first decide what information he requires. If, for example, the structure is to be a bare warehouse building where settlement would go almost unnoticed, there is no need for consolidation tests. The values of shear strength at various depths, the geological nature of the strata and their past history, an examination of the material in the hand and an establishing of its classification would give all the information required. If, on the other hand, the building is a concert hall of fine construction and delicate finishes, a greater depth of exploration is justifiable, and the information to be obtained should be comprehensive. The first of these explorations should be only a fraction of the cost of the second, yet one often finds elaborate tests made where no such tests are justified by the quality, type and value of the building. Naturally, in the absence of detailed instructions, investigating firms, moving into an unfamiliar site from a distance, make all possible tests, even if the local architect has an extensive, if subjective, knowledge of the strata of the area.

6.3. Depth and Extent of the Exploration

The depth to which the exploration of the site should be taken depends on the mass of soil which is affected by the weight of the building. It might be well at this point to glance at the section on *bulbs of pressure* in Chapter 4. The effect of the added pressure on the surface occasioned by the building is not dispersed to an insignificant value until a depth is reached equal to several times the width of the foundations applying the load. The exploration must, therefore, go to a depth at which, in the architect's opinion, the bulb of pressure shows that the residual effect is insignificant and, in his opinion, has no further effect on the soil. It is axiomatic that the exploration for a wide footing—perhaps a raft—must go much deeper than that for simple pad footings. Also, if a complex of buildings is in question the depth of site investigation can be varied to suit each building in the group. This has the effect of substantially reducing the cost of the investigation, for there is little need of borings to 50 or 60 feet for a sports hall founded on pad footings widely spaced, even if such depths are required for a three-storey building nearby founded on a raft.

Such decisions on depth must be based on what the architect intends to do when the foundations are designed. Granted that it is not possible to design the foundations fully unless there is good knowledge of the strata encountered, yet some estimation must commence the design. It is much less costly to estimate the types of footings which the architect would like to see installed, or thinks may be necessary, than to demand a full site investigation to all possible depths and with all possible tests before any information on the substructure is made available.

The most economic technique, therefore, is, first, for the architect to make at least sketch decisions on the types of foundation he intends to install. These decisions will depend on the buildings themselves, on local knowledge of the soil, on geological conditions, and on previous case histories of buildings nearby. From these tentative sketches, a plan of campaign for the site exploration can be made, the extent of the investigation being adapted to the particular building of the complex. If, later, the arrangement or type of building is altered, a further site investigation may be necessary. This should be avoided if at all possible, for it is expensive to start again. For this reason, it is best to wait before commencing the site investigation until the complex of buildings is firmly decided as to placing and type. The substructures should be in sketch form rather than developed to working drawings. On receipt of the details he has asked for in the site report, the architect can produce final designs. If he is wise he will keep a running watch on the results coming from the site investigation even before the report is produced so that he can issue instructions for changes in the programme as required by the conditions revealed.

The acceptance of the basic dimension of "twice the breadth of the footing" as the depth to which exploration should be taken, means that the use of trial pits and test loadings on the surface can give highly misleading information. Trial pits, by their nature, can extend only a short distance into the mass of soil to be affected by the weight of the structure. They cannot reveal strata at some distance below the surface the characteristics of which may have a deleterious effect on settlement or bearing capacity. Test loadings on small plates produce only shallow bulbs of pressure which, again, cannot exert the effect on the soil which is later applied by the larger bulb of pressure induced by the whole building. Test pits and surface test loads are useful for structures with shallow foundations, such as houses or highways, where the effect of loading does not penetrate deeply; otherwise, small diameter borings must remain the basic method of exploration.

Borings have disadvantages; the soil cannot be seen *in situ*, samples are not as easy to extract as from a trial pit and some soils, such as saturated sand, can be brought up from a borehole in the same state as it exists in the ground only by the greatest ingenuity. Borings must go deeply into the bulb of pressure to be efficient; to take them only to depths to which a trial pit could go is not sensible.

6.4. Cost and Interpretation

One of the reasons why site investigations are carried out too timidly and inefficiently is their cost. Some expense must be planned for this necessary preliminary work, but, if directed with knowledge, the investigation can be kept to a minimum cost relative to the type of construction envisaged. It cannot be too firmly repeated that a site investigation is always advisable and worthwhile. Its cost is small in proportion to the cost of the building. It is unwise to embark on the construction of foundations without knowing not only the average type of soil and its likely behaviour, but also the variations which occur across the site. The object of this chapter is to assist the architect to avoid the two faults of, on the one hand, carrying out no site investigation at all and, on the other, being presented with a costly report on an investigation unrelated to the needs of the building to be erected.

The first step in trying to eliminate unnecessary cost in site exploration is to have some idea of the type of strata and soil likely to be encountered. A good guide to this may be given by geological conditions. The area may be in a region which suffered a heavy load of ice during the ice ages or where a great depth of superincumbent strata have been later eroded away. It may be in some region where the landscape has not suffered either denudation or deposition, or it may lie on a recently deposited (in geological terms) stratum. All these indications help in deciding the type of investigation required. Where earlier loading has existed on the soil, the clays (which cause the foundation troubles) will be overconsolidated, of good strength and insensitive to remoulding. Piling into such clay may be good practice. Where the clays are normally consolidated, merely by their own weight, a lower cohesion and a higher coefficient of compressibility are to be expected.

When we come to consider interpretation, the architect's concern with site investigation is not so much in the technicalities and the methods of carrying out the investigation as with the methods of obtaining, from the results, information suited to his purposes. It is assumed in this chapter that the architect will not carry out the investigation himself, although there is no reason why some of the simpler tests could not be carried out by the architect's staff. When the report comes in, the architect should find what he expects to find; his specification of the tests to be carried out should have been complied with, and a sufficient number of tests should have been specified and done to give an adequate statistical interpretation not only of average strengths and consolidation characteristics, but also of the variations encountered. In a site investigation report recently seen by the author, only four consolidation tests were made at shallow depths and were, therefore, not of any use in interpreting the effect of loading on settlement. If a course of testing is embarked upon it must be carried out so that interpretation can at least be attempted. Chapters 2, 3 and 5 give guidance on the type of information needed, and Chapters 7, 8 and 9 indicate how that information can be applied to the determination of the significant features of the foundations. The figures in Chapter 4, having been calculated from theory based on assumptions, are not influenced by the results of the site investigation.

This chapter has been placed between those specifying properties and tests, and those concerned with settlement and bearing capacity, for it is here that site investigation belongs. The architect should first decide from Chapters 2, 3 and 5 what he wants to know, make sure that he gets reliable figures and then turn, himself, to Chapters 7, 8 and 9 and apply the results of the site investigation to his own needs.

6.5. Placing of Boreholes

It is unwise to define, too exactly, the number and location of boreholes at the beginning of the investigation. Sometimes, from the results of the first explorations, it is found that more holes are needed to clarify a puzzling phenomenon. Sometimes the depths of holes may have to be altered while the work is going on, and some may be stopped if sufficient information is available from the others. This requires that the daily log sheets of the investigation should be examined as they are produced and the necessary instructions given there and then. Too often the architect's first contact with the site investigation is when the report comes in; it is too late then if it is found that important data are missing.

Figure 6.1 shows the strata obtained by a series of boreholes spaced across a valley. From the way in which the sand layers appeared in these holes and from knowledge of the regional geology extra boreholes were ordered. It was fortunate that this order was given, for the hole showed a steep dip of the sand into a buried valley. As the site was intended for a dam, construction based on the first diagram would have resulted in leakage below the dam, whereas the information in the second diagram allowed of proper provision being made. The extra cost of the final boreholes was insignificant compared with the expense saved.

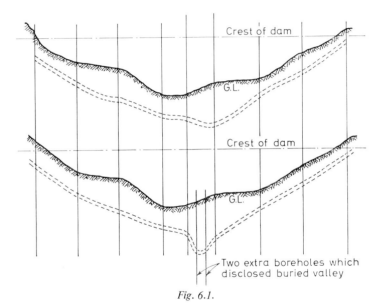

Fig. 6.1.

In areas of glacial drift and boulder clay, the striking of rock must always be looked upon with suspicion. In the past, boulders have been assumed to represent rock-head with very serious consequences. When "rock" is struck in such soil even boring into it for a short distance is no guarantee of its nature. Only another borehole nearby can show whether rock is continuous at that level or that a boulder is present. Preliminary geophysical tests could give some indication of continuous hard layers. Again, the cost of the extra hole or the cost of geophysical exploration is an insurance against costly mistakes.

There should be at least one borehole driven below any building in a group, and for long or wide buildings the number of boreholes per building must be increased to ensure that the variation in strata, both laterally and vertically, is properly recorded. Many mistakes have been made by basing construction on a tenuous or restricted boring programme.

6.6. Sampling

The architect is not concerned with the techniques used in extracting samples but he should understand the significance of the types of sample extracted. Two kinds of specimen can be taken from boreholes—*disturbed* or *jar samples*, and *undisturbed samples*. The jar sample is easily obtained and is a quantity or a piece of the soil in question placed in a jar with a screw-top lid to prevent change in condition or moisture content. These samples amount in quantity to a fistful of material, and can be used for the determination of *moisture content* (at least for approximate values), *liquid limit, plastic limit* and *classification* (if the sample is big enough). These are tests for which the soil is deliberately disturbed, and a disturbed sample is adequate for the purpose. These samples also allow of visual inspection, which forms a useful means of building up a mental picture of site conditions. Small portions of clay rubbed between the fingers (or between the front teeth!) can be tentatively placed in the plasticity chart and so judged for possible properties. The architect should never rely merely on the formal report on the site exploration but should inspect jar samples and relate what he observes to the recommendations made in the report.

The *undisturbed sample* is intended to show the material as it exists in the stratum at the bottom of the borehole. Such a sample is extracted carefully, and the sampling tube immediately sealed at both ends with paraffin wax to prevent changes in the natural state of the soil. The object is that the tests (Chapters 2 and 5) can be carried out on the soil as it will be found when excavation is made. The assumption is made that the values obtained in the tests are those the soil will exhibit when stressed by the weight of the building. Since it is impossible to remove a 4-inch sample by forcing the sampling tube through the soil without disturbing its form and nature, the term "undisturbed" should be accepted with reserve. For granular soils the practical difficulties in obtaining a sample even approaching the true nature of the soil are very great. The further the soil departs from the pure clay and approaches the gravel-end of the classification chart, the more unlikely it is that the sample is truly "undisturbed".

Samples for test—undisturbed samples—should be extracted at every five feet (at least) and also at every change in stratum. Only by a thorough testing at closely spaced intervals can any confidence be placed in the predictions made from the exploration. A few widely spaced tests cannot show trends or changes in properties with depth. Examples of the many tests required are shown in the figures accompanying the problems CP9A and CP9B; these are from the author's practice.

6.7. *Tests* in situ

Because of the difficulties of sampling and testing granular soils (with any approach to reliability) by means of "undisturbed" samples taken from boreholes, methods of testing such soils as they are encountered at the bottom of the boreholes have been devised. In countries where there are many occurrences of sandy and gravelly soil empirical penetration tests have been used. These are either static (in which a conical shoe is pushed into the sandy soil and the resistance to penetration measured) or dynamic (in which a sampling "spoon" is driven into the soil by blows of a standard energy value). The resistance to penetration, either static or dynamic, is matched empirically to the ability of the sand layer to sustain load.

From the United States came the *standard penetration test*, also used in other countries. A weight of 140 lb is dropped through a height of 30 inches and the number of blows required to drive the sampling spoon into the soil for a depth of a foot is counted. This, again, gives a measure of the bearing capacity of the soil (Chapter 7). Instructions should always be given for a standard penetration test to be made when sand or gravel is encountered in a borehole.

Although it is an empirical test, and one giving only approximate results, it allows comparison between different strata to be made.

Some clays, especially those which are normally consolidated, have their strength much reduced if they are disturbed. These are called sensitive clays, the sensitivity being measured by the ratio:

$$\frac{\text{Cohesive strength of the undisturbed sample}}{\text{Cohesive strength of a disturbed and remoulded sample}}.$$

This figure can go up to as much as 8 or more showing how much strength is lost by destruction of the sensitive skeleton of the clay. Heavily overconsolidated clays may have a sensitivity of unity, showing that they are not affected by remoulding, having been disturbed already in geological times.

For sensitive clays, as for the difficult granular soils, *in situ* tests probably give a more reliable value of strength than do tests on "undisturbed" samples. The test used is the *shear vane test* as described in Chapter 5. This test should be specified, at least as a check on sample tests, if the soil is suspected of being sensitive.

Such *in situ* tests as the vane test and the standard penetration test are likely to increase the architect's knowledge of the nature of his foundation material in such a way as to help in producing accurate prediction of behaviour. Other *in situ* tests which have been, and are, popular—loading tests in an inspection pit and loading tests on a single pile—may often be more misleading than helpful. Plate-bearing tests in highway construction are acceptable and give useful information because only a relatively small depth is concerned and the loading is light. The disadvantage of the plate-bearing test for building foundations has been mentioned above.

Where a test load on a pile gives figures of loading and settlement, it would seem logical to multiply the loading by the number of piles in the group to determine how much a closely spaced pile grouping can carry, and to accept the settlement of the pile as the value of the settlement of the group. Experience shows that a group of piles carries much less load than this kind of calculation defines, and also that a pile group in sand may settle a great deal more (cases of up to 10 times have been recorded) than the settlement of a single pile under the same loading. Loading tests can give indications of value, but the results must not be taken at face value, and must be interpreted with care.

6.8. Tests to be Specified for Foundation Design

The tests which can be considered as generally required whatever the type of building are the *classification tests*. Clays, particularly, should always be classified, especially with reference to the plasticity chart. *Plastic and liquid limits* and *natural moisture contents* give a great deal of information; the tests are easy to carry out and should always be specified. For granular soils a *particle-size analysis* is also essential.

When we consider *bearing capacity*, the architect is interested in the strength of the soil immediately the load is applied. The *immediate tests* are, therefore, his particular concern. Any strength which is achieved by the soil after loading can be looked upon as an insurance against further settlement and cracking. The consolidated shear tests (Chapter 5) are not of a great deal of interest. It is during and immediately after construction that the conditions must be safe. He thus requires, for any stratum suspected of weakness, the *cohesion*, *angle of shearing resistance*, *bulk density* and the *depth* at which the footing is to be placed. If it is known that settlement of the building will not cause much concern these values (in sufficient number to give a clear picture of variations), together with classification values, will allow of an allowable bearing pressure being calculated by the rapid but approximate method of Chapter 9 (see Fig. 9.1). The cost of consolidation tests can be eliminated.

If *consolidation tests* are specified because settlement is of importance, then there must, again, be an adequate number of them to give clear information. It is not enough to take two or three and then report that "this shows great variation". The extent and nature of the variation must be predicted, for on this depends the safety of the building. The fact that variation occurs is the reason for *more* tests, not fewer. Coefficients of compressibility and consolidation should be obtained throughout the clay layers under the building and sufficient tests carried out to give a statistical measure of the probability of settlement.

If the clay layers underlying a building site are known to be pure clays, and this can be judged from the jar samples as the investigation proceeds, definite instructions about shear testing should be given.

For such clays the *unconfined compression test* gives adequate values of shear strength. One often sees reports on site investigations in which time, money and effort have been spent in elaborate triaxial compression testing when the results show that this elaboration is unnecessary. One or two triaxial tests followed by unconfined com-

Table 6A

Visible state of soil from jar samples	Problem to be solved	Tests to be made, both field and laboratory	Types of foundation to which these refer
Soft, normally consolidated clay	Bearing capacity; settlement	Vane shear; cohesion from undisturbed samples; L.L., P.L., classification; consolidation	ALL THE
Stiff, perhaps overconsolidated clay	Bearing capacity; settlement	Cohesion from undisturbed samples; L.L., P.L., classification; consolidation	TYPES OF FOOTING
Sandy or gravelly clay with stones of some size	Bearing capacity; settlement; permeability	Plate-bearing test of some help; remoulded samples; unconfined compr. test on soil binder; L.L., P.L., on fine fraction of soil particles; permeability	TREATED IN THIS BOOK
Sands and gravels	Bearing capacity; permeability and flow of ground water	Penetration tests; triaxial or shear-box tests on samples at original density	

pression tests when ϕ has been proved equal to zero for the immediate loading will reduce the cost of site investigation and speed the production of the report. The more the architect is in control of the site investigation the more will be his understanding of his foundation conditions. Table 6A gives a guiding pattern which may be useful, but should not be looked upon as restrictive or comprehensive.

6.9. Tests for Sulphates

Since most foundation substructures contain concrete or mortar in some form, the site investigation should never be wound up without an investigation of the presence of sulphates in ground water. These chemicals corrode and can utterly disintegrate portland cement concrete. Sulphate content, if it is present at all, tends to increase with depth. In such soils there is much to be said for keeping the depth of foundation small. It should be remembered, however, that, like other aspects of soil on building sites, the content of sulphates can vary considerably from point to point and in depth. Seasonal variations are also prominent. Table 6B gives some indication of the type of precautions which should be taken, as put forward by Bessey and Lea who made a very thorough study of the problem at numerous sites.

Table 6B

	Amount of sulphate in clay foundations		Precautions to be taken with concrete buried in and surrounded by clay
Class	In groundwater	In clay	
	(SO_3 per 100,000)	($\% SO_3$ in air-dried clay)	
1	Less than 30	Less than 0·2	No special measures. Lean concrete inadvisable if SO_3 in water exceeds 20 parts per 100,000
2	30 to 100	0·2 to 0·5	Rich, dense concrete unlikely to be seriously affected over short period of years. For most foundation work the use of concrete containing pozzolanic, sulphate-resisting, super-sulphated or high-alumina cement is advisable
3	More than 100	More than 0·5	Use of high-alumina or super-sulphated cement concretes is recommended

PART III

DESIGN FOR STABILITY

Ultimate Bearing Capacity
Limitation of Settlement
Allowable Bearing Pressure

Chapter 7

Ultimate Bearing Capacity

7.1. Terms Used

In all discussions of the design of foundations for stability and safety, the architect must be clear as to the exact meanings of the terms used. He must also use these terms exactly, remembering that there are two kinds of failure causing structural damage. These are mentioned in Chapter 1, since they are the principal subjects towards which the work of this book is directed. The soil, under the excess loading caused by a foundation, may fail suddenly and even catastrophically by a shear failure, or it may settle slowly by the consolidation of the foundation material until the movement is so great as to cause structural damage. Both of these possible types of failure must be allowed for in the design and prevented as far as possible. The architect's ideal would be to load the soil in such a way that the stresses developed by the soil in resistance to the excess loading would cause no movement at all. This is a counsel of perfection, for it is unlikely that there will be no movement of any kind unless the building is founded on rock. Settlement is the normal condition and is studied in Chapter 8. A shear failure, which is the subject of this chapter, must not be allowed to occur. It always results in serious damage.

The loads which relate to different conditions of movement or of stability are given quite definite descriptions which are internationally accepted in English-speaking countries. They are as follows:

Ultimate Bearing Capacity is the value of the nett loading intensity, or the pressure applied by the footing, which causes the ground to fail suddenly in shear. Such a value of the bearing capacity could not be used in the design of the foundations. To ensure safety, a load factor or factor of safety must be applied.

Maximum Safe Bearing Capacity is obtained by dividing the ultimate bearing capacity by a factor of safety. It is the maximum nett loading intensity which may be safely carried without the risk of shear failure. This may not be the value finally used in designing the foundations of the building; even the "safe" bearing capacity may be sufficiently high to give a risk of excessive settlement and damage due to differential settlement.

Allowable Bearing Pressure is the value which is used in design, and which takes into account all the possibilities of failure, including possible structural damage due to consolidation settlement. This is frequently less than the safe bearing capacity.

In this chapter only the first two steps of finding the maximum and safebearing capacities are taken. The studies of Chapter 8 help towards the determination of allowable bearing pressure. The work of this chapter merely eliminates the risk of catastrophic shear failure, but is not concerned with the effects of consolidation settlement.

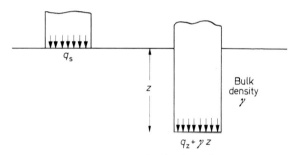

Fig. 7.1.   Nett loading intensity.

Before commencing study of the value of the ultimate bearing capacity it is appropriate to consider the effect of the overburden pressure and what is meant by the nett loading intensity. In Fig. 7.1 there are two footings of equal dimensions. If the maximum safe bearing capacity of a strip load on the surface is q_s and for a similar strip at a depth z is q_z, then the latter will be somewhat higher than q_s because of the surcharge effect of the soil surrounding the deeper loading plate. But at the deeper depth the soil was first *unloaded* when the excavation was made and this pressure (represented by the bulk density multiplied by the depth) can be added to the nett loading intensity to give the pressure that the base of the excavation can carry safely.

7.2. Variation in Bearing Capacity

One might assume that, if a soil is uniform in properties and composition over a wide area and to a great depth (the ideal soil of Chapter 4), the bearing capacity of this soil could hardly fail to be constant. It might be expected to be a property of the material and applicable in all circumstances. This idea—that a soil has a unique bearing capacity—is widespread among architects, and is even applied to soils which are manifestly far from uniform. Such a conception, however, is too simple for the complexity of the problem. The architect must realize that the values of the ultimate and safe bearing capacities depend, not only on the properties of the soil, but also on the type of foundation it is intended to use. There are at least four properties of the footing as applied to the soil which can alter the value of the ultimate bearing capacity and therefore of the allowable bearing pressure to be used in design. These factors are the length and breadth of the footing, the shape (circular, rectangular, etc.), the depth at which the footing is placed, and the roughness of the material used for its construction, particularly on the underside of the pad which rests on the soil. For a given type of footing placed in various types of soil, the ultimate bearing capacity varies with the properties of the soil—its frictional resistance, its cohesion, its density and the classification to which it belongs (Chapter 2). Remembering, therefore, that the dimensions and design of the footing applying the load to the soil have a considerable influence on the bearing capacity of the soil, it is illogical to ask for a value of bearing capacity to be developed from the results of site investigation without first at least suggesting the type of foundation likely to be chosen for the stanchions. In any consideration of ultimate bearing capacity, therefore, the type of foundation should be described and the *shear* properties of the soil should be known (Chapter 5). The characteristics of permeability, compressibility and consolidation of the soil are not required at this stage, but are needed in determining the allowable bearing pressure, when the settlement is considered.

7.3. Mechanism of Shear Failure

Many investigators have studied behaviour of the soil as it gives way to a load producing sudden shear failure. Considerable arguments have raged over the exact shape of the disturbed volume of soil and on the value to be placed on its resistance to failure. These controversies need not concern the architect closely, although he may like to follow the discussion in the pages of the technical press devoted to soil mechanics. Figure 7.2 gives a generally agreed picture of the disturbance and failure of the soil which occurs when a footing applying its load at the surface, or very closely below the surface, fails and sinks into the ground.

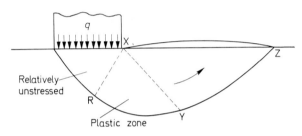

Fig. 7.2.   Mechanism of shear failure.

The failure zone consists of three parts. There is first a kind of wedge underneath the footing which is relatively undisturbed, and which may be looked upon as a triangular "shoe" driving down into the mass of soil. Immediately next to this unaffected zone there is a zone which is under plastic failure by shear. The slipping of one portion of the soil on another probably starts at some point within this zone, and the shear failure spreads until the whole zone is in a state of plastic flow (RXY). The third zone is XYZ which represents a mass of soil being pushed outwards and upwards by the plastic failure of XYR. Theoretically, this failure ought to occur simultaneously on all sides of the footing if the soil is of uniform properties and the loading is truly vertical. Usually, however, in practice, if such a failure does take place (and they are relatively rare because of precautions taken against settlement) it occurs on one side only because of the slight lack of symmetry which affects even the best arrangement of stanchion and footing.

When we come to consider deep footing, that is, footings founded at a depth greater than the width of the footing, we find some discrepancy between the theories advanced by various authorities. No unanimity of opinion has as yet been developed; although much laboratory experiment has been carried out, the number of documented cases of shear failure of deep foundations is very small. In calculating the ultimate bearing capacity by various methods, the architect must still use his own judgement in making his decision. As has already been pointed out, calculations in soil mechanics are guides rather than masters of design.

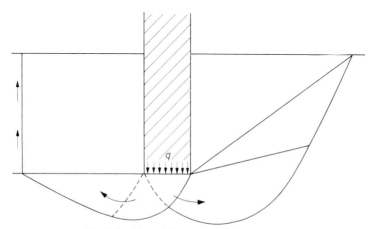

Fig. 7.3.   Shear failure in deep foundations.

Figure 7.3 shows two conceptions of the type of failure pattern which may occur under strip footings founded at some depth below the surface. The left-hand diagram shows the assumed mechanism calculated by Terzaghi, who considered that the shear strength of the overburden above the level of the deep foundation was of less significance. The right-hand diagram is by Meyerhof, who used a different and perhaps more accurate assumption for the shape of the disturbed volume of soil when the failure takes place. Finality has not been reached, and mathematical calculations of the type which led to Fig. 7.3 must be checked against more recorded examples of shear failure before it can be said that we know undoubtedly what occurs in deep foundations. Not enough such failures have been reported or investigated.

7.4. Bearing Capacity Factors

From the mathematical investigation of ultimate bearing capacity, and from experimental work, a number of factors have been developed. These *bearing capacity factors* are used to determine the influence of the various characteristics of soil and footing on the value of the ultimate bearing capacity. Terzaghi, who was the first to propose the use of bearing capacity factors, divided the total value of the ultimate bearing capacity into three parts, each of these parts originating in some property of the soil and of the depth of the footing (so long as this was not greater than its width). The three properties concerned are *cohesion, density* and *overburden pressure* exerted by the soil at the depth of the foundation.

The three original bearing capacity coefficients are:

N_c, which controls the effect of cohesion in the final estimate of ultimate bearing capacity,

N_q, which controls the effect of overburden pressure at the level at which the foundation is placed and

N_γ, which controls the effect of the density of the soil.

Since Terzaghi's original calculation of the bearing capacity factors, other research workers and mathematicians have developed different values for these original three, and have also worked out other bearing capacity factors for special situations. Bearing capacity factors have also been combined to give the linked effect of various aspects of the problem. Other important bearing capacity factors which are encountered are:

N_{cq}, which controls the combined effect of cohesion and foundation depth and

$N_{\gamma q}$, which controls the combined effect of density and foundation depth.

Controversy still rages about the values of these coefficients, although it is agreed that the method involving the use of such devices is the very best way of determining at least an estimate of the ultimate bearing capacity of soil and footing. Discrepancies between the work of individual observers exist, and the architect must make the final decision.

7.5. Calculation of Bearing Capacity

The estimated ultimate bearing capacity using Terzaghi's bearing capacity factors and the measured properties of the soil is given by the expression:

$$\text{Ultimate bearing capacity} = cN_c + \gamma z N_q + 0.5 \, \gamma B N_\gamma.$$

The parameters of greatest importance in this estimation are the *breadth of the footing*, the *angle of shearing resistance* and the *cohesion*. The other properties listed in the previous section are also important, but these three are of particular significance. It may be asked why the angle of shearing resistance has not, so far, been mentioned, if it is of such importance. The reason lies in the fact that the bearing capacity factors are dependent *only* on the angle of shearing resistance. The greater the angle, the greater the value of all the factors, and thus, the greater the value of the ultimate bearing capacity.

The procedure in using bearing capacity factors is to determine for the soil the *cohesion*, *angle of shearing resistance* and *density* and, for the footing, its *breadth* and the *depth* at which it is founded. This must be less than the breadth of the footing; Terzaghi's coefficients apply to a strip footing founded at a shallow depth. The values of the three bearing capacity factors are read off from Fig. 7.4, and the various data inserted in the above expression for ultimate bearing capacity.

7.6. Variations on Terzaghi's Original Conception

Many mathematicians and experimental research workers have studied this subject both before and after Terzaghi. It would be out of place in this introductory volume, and even misleading, to attempt to compare and assess these various solutions. One other authority on this topic may, however, be quoted to show the direction in which research is progressing. Meyerhof's assessment of the values of bearing capacity factors for strip loadings is shown by the dotted lines in Fig. 7.4.

For deeply founded footings not covered by Terzaghi's bearing capacity factors, Meyerhof has developed other factors shown in

Fig. 7.5. In Fig. 7.6 his values for square footings are shown. Other variations of loading which might result in different values of bearing capacity factors are known, and special values apply when the soil is purely cohesive or purely frictional. Then, the bearing capacity factors can be combined for speedier solution.

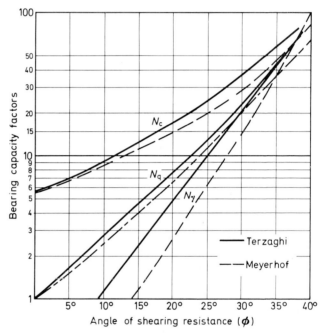

Fig. 7.4.   Bearing capacity factors; shallow strip load.

7.7. *Effect of the Shape of the Footing*

The basic figures for bearing capacity have usually been worked out for strip footings which allows of a two-dimensional study. As the strip footing is assumed to be infinitely long, a "slice" can be cut off and examined without reference to the third dimension. However, when the strip is of a short length—when the footing is rectangular or square—the effect of the support given by the soil at the ends of the footing must be taken into account, and the foundation has a higher ultimate bearing capacity. Much of the opinion developed on how such three-dimensional considerations should be brought into the final result comes from experimental research on model footings. When the soil under a strip footing fails in shear, the movement is laterally outward. If a square, rectangular or circular footing fails, the movement of soil particles forms a radial pattern. This three-dimensional support means that a rectangular or circular footing

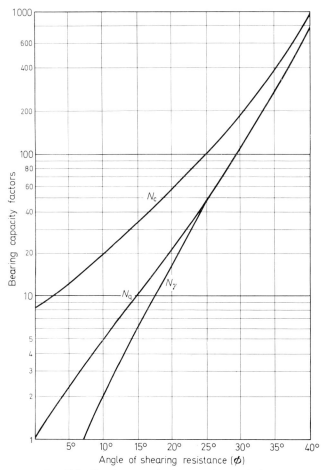

Fig. 7.5.   Bearing capacity factors; deep strip load.

must be loaded to a higher intensity, before it fails, than is necessary for a strip footing. The question to be decided is by how much the strip value should be multiplied to give a three-dimensional effect. The most recent work tends to show that the figure depends on the ratio of the length to the breadth of a rectangular footing, and Skempton gives: *For a rectangle, the ultimate bearing capacity is equal to the ultimate bearing capacity for a strip, multiplied by:*

$$(1 + 0.2\ B/L).$$

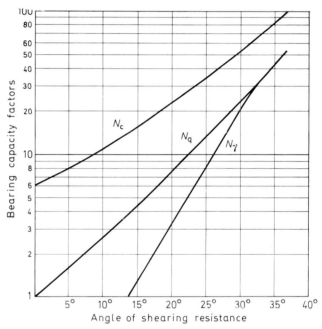

Fig. 7.6.   Bearing capacity factors; square footings.

If B is equal to L as in a square, the multiplier is 1·2. This is a maximum, for as the breadth decreases, so does the multiplier. Terzaghi gives:

$$\text{U.B.C. for a square} = 1.3\ cN_c + \gamma z N_q + 0.4\ \gamma B N_\gamma$$

and

$$\text{U.B.C. for a circle} = 1.3\ cN_c + \gamma z N_q + 0.6\ \gamma B N_\gamma.$$

In normal circumstances for smaller buildings, an estimation of the safe bearing capacity for a strip footing increased by 20% to 30% gives a sufficiently reliable figure.

7.8. Bearing Capacity of Piled Foundations

The architect's reaction when confronted with an apparently difficult site is too often to hand the matter over to a specialist piling firm. Although piles may often result in a stable foundation, and may form an insurance against the settlement of a large and important building, they are not invariably the correct support for the more normal type of small building. In the author's experience, foundations for schools and other buildings of this kind can be completed successfully on sites where even piles would support very little load.

Further, the type of material of which the ground is composed is important. If the soil is a sensitive clay, piles, unless they bear on a solid stratum, will do more damage than would occur if they had been omitted. The remoulding of sensitive, normally consolidated clays results in loss of strength and in the tendency towards greater settlement. In heavily overconsolidated clays piles will be helpful; once again a knowledge of the geological history of the area is of value.

Piles which bear on a gravel or rock stratum merely carry the load to a lower level, and it is at this level that any calculations of settlement and bearing capacity should be made. Even this type of bearing has its problems. In Mexico City, for example, there are many instances of buildings damaged because of the use of piles. Figure 7.7 shows a sketch of the situation. The whole depth of material SR is highly sensitive to the abstraction of water by pressure or by pumping. Some buildings, founded on the surface, have shown large settlements due to their own weight.

Other buildings were, later, built on piles founded on a granular stratum some distance below the surface, in order to eliminate this consolidation settlement. However, as water supply from the city was being abstracted from deep aquifers, the water table was lowered and consolidation settlement took place (see Problem CP8C). The buildings founded on the surface settled with the surface, but those on piles settled a smaller amount, solely on account of the consolidation of the lower part of the soil (GR). The result has been that buildings on point-bearing piles have, apparently, risen out of the ground, some of them by several feet. This is, of course, a special situation where the soil has a very high void ratio and consolidates rapidly even under low loads, but it indicates the necessity of understanding the mechanism of support and failure.

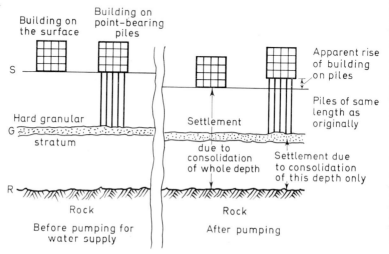

Fig. 7.7   Point bearing piles and general settlement.

The type of pile which is of greater interest from the point of view of the mechanics of soil is the *friction pile*. Here, the bearing capacity of the circular base could be estimated by the methods of this chapter, but it has been found from experience that the greater part of the load carried is borne by the friction along the sides of the pile. The bearing capacity of the ends is much less significant.

There is no way in which this frictional load can be estimated by calculation. The soil is violently disturbed during driving and during the construction of a bored pile and it is quite impossible to analyse what effect this has on skin friction. Only loading tests can give information on which a design can be based, but the architect must not be deluded by the apparent simplicity of this method. A group of closely spaced piles will not, for example, support a load equal to the number of piles multiplied by the test value of one pile. The group load will be less. How much less is still a subject of argument the proportion varying with the circumstances. A group of piles in sand may also settle up to 10 times as much as does a single test pile. An empirical approach is the only way of tackling the problem of foundations on friction piles. Before piles are finally chosen as the method of support in bad ground other techniques, such as the improvement of the properties of the soil or the use of buoyant foundations, should be investigated.

7.9. Bearing Capacity of Soils at Extreme Range of Classification

Soils which are pure clays with no granular material at all, or purely granular with no cohesive material, form special cases. For purely cohesive soils the first term, only, of the Terzaghi expression need be used. For granular soils, only the last term is needed.

For purely granular soil another factor comes into the picture, the relationship of breadth of footing to the depth at which it is placed. For cohesive soils after a value of about 2 to 3 this ratio has no appreciable effect. The value of N_{cq} (which is the sole B.C.F. needed) varies from 5·7 (Fig. 7.4) for $z/B = 0$ to about 8 (Meyerhof) or 7·5 (Skempton) when the depth is about 3 times the breadth of the footing.

For granular soils, however, the effect is much more important. The bearing capacity factor to be used with the last term of the equation when the soil is purely granular ($N_{\gamma q}$) increases rapidly as the depth/breadth ratio increases. For example, Meyerhof estimates that for a granular soil with an angle of shearing resistance of 30° the low value (15–20) for N_γ shown in Fig. 7.4 can increase to 1000 by the time the depth/breadth ratio is about 20.

7.10. Bearing Capacity by Penetration Methods

It is somewhat academic to discuss angles of shearing resistance for purely granular material, for it is very difficult—one could almost say impossible—to obtain a truly undisturbed sample for test. The angle of shearing resistance as the soil lies in the ground (or at the bottom of a borehole) must be tested *in situ* if it is to have any true significance.

The method most in use is the *Standard Penetration Test* discussed in Chapter 6. The number of blows required to drive the sampling "spoon" through the sand for one foot gives a measure of the density of the sand. Any number of blows greater than 50 indicates a very dense sand. Anything below 10 shows a loose sand. From this rather vague measure of quality some estimate can be made of the ability of the sand to carry load. The number of blows is recorded as N.

Terzaghi and Peck give, as an example, a safe bearing capacity for a 5-ft foundation of 6 ton/ft^2 when N is 50 or more. As the width of the footing increases, the value of 6 drops to below 5 ton/ft^2 (by the time 20-ft wide footings are in question). At the other end of the scale (a loose sand with $N = 10$) the safe bearing pressure is down to about 1 ton/ft^2 for all widths, the decrease of bearing capacity with increase in width being small.

All this presupposes that the sand is dry or moist. If the water table rises to within twice the breadth of the footing from the underside of the foundation, then the bearing capacity is much reduced. Flooding of a sandy foundation may decrease the bearing capacity to one-half of its original value because of the increase in pore pressure and the consequent decrease in effective pressure. Flooding of a clay foundation has no immediate appreciable effect.

An approximate correlation between the *Standard Penetration Resistance* and the angle of shearing resistance is given in Table 7A. From these values of ϕ bearing capacity factors can be determined and the ultimate bearing capacity of the footing estimated.

Table 7A

State of granular material	Standard penetration resistance (Number of blows)	Angle of shearing resistance
Very loose	Less than 4	Less than 30°
Loose	4–10	30°–35°
Medium	10–30	35°–40°
Dense	30–50	40°–45°
Very dense	Greater than 50	Greater than 45°

COMPUTATION PANELS SEVEN

Prerequisite reading: Chapter 7 and Sections 2.2, 2.7, 5.2, 5.3

Reminders
Ultimate bearing capacity
Safe bearing capacity } must be used accurately
Allowable bearing pressure
Bearing capacity factor controlling effect of cohesion: N_c
Bearing capacity factor controlling effect of overburden pressure: N_q
Bearing capacity factor controlling effect of density: N_γ
Breadth of footing: B (length)
Depth from surface to level of footing: z (length)
Number of blows in Standard Penetration Test: N

CP7A
PROBLEM: To determine the ultimate and safe bearing capacities of a strip footing founded on a purely cohesive clay at a shallow depth

Data
Samples of the clay were tested in unconfined compression and the following results obtained from 7 samples: Failing stress was 8·2, 7·9, 8·4, 9·0, 8·1, 8·8, 8·0 lb/in². The footing is 4 feet wide and founded at a depth of 3 ft. Bulk density = 110 lb/ft³.

Results required
(a) The ultimate bearing capacity of the footing.
(b) The safe bearing capacity of the footing using a factor of safety of 2·5.

Method of attack
(1) For a purely cohesive soil the apparent cohesion or shear strength is one-half of the unconfined compressive strength (Chapter 5). The mean compressive strength is 8·3 lb/in², and the apparent cohesion is, therefore, about 4·2 lb/in², or 600 lb/ft².
(2) For a purely cohesive soil, only the first two terms of Terzaghi's equation are relevant:
$$q = cN_c + \gamma z N_q.$$

(3) Substituting the properties of the soil and the depth of the footing, and using $N_c = 5.7$ and $N_q = 1$ which are the values of the bearing capacity coefficients, we have:

Ultimate bearing capacity 3750 lb/ft^2 and (dividing by 2.5):

Safe bearing capacity 1500 lb/ft^2.

(4) The relief given by the excavation must now be added to give:

Ultimate bearing capacity 4080 lb/ft^2.
Safe bearing capacity 1830 lb/ft^2.

CP7B

PROBLEM: To determine the ultimate bearing capacity of a strip footing on a homogeneous soil

Data

The strip footing is 10 feet wide and is based at a depth of 6 ft in soil with an apparent cohesion of 600 lb/ft^2 and an angle of shearing resistance of $10°$. The bulk density of the soil is 120 lb/ft^3.

Results required

(a) Ultimate bearing capacity of the footing.
(b) Safe bearing capacity using a factor of safety of 3.

Method of attack

(1) The footing is not founded deeper than its width and can thus be considered as a shallow strip footing for which Terzaghi's fundamental equation applies:

$$q = cN_c + \gamma z N_q + 0.5\, \gamma B N_\gamma.$$

(2) Substitute the values of the known properties in the equation:

$$q = 600\, N_c + 720\, N_q + 600\, N_\gamma.$$

(3) Look up Fig. 7.4 to determine the values of the bearing capacity coefficients, and complete the equation:

$$q = 600 \times 10 + 720 \times 4 + 600 \times 2.$$

(4) The ultimate bearing capacity according to Terzaghi is 10,080 lb/ft^2 and the safe bearing capacity (dividing by 3) is 3360 lb/ft^2.

(5) To *both* these values must be added the relief afforded to the soil by the 6 ft of excavation. Thus the ultimate and safe bearing capacities at the level at which the footing is founded, are:

$$10,080 + 720 = 10,800 \text{ lb/ft}^2 \text{ (ultimate)}$$
$$\text{and} \qquad 3360 + 720 = 4080 \text{ lb/ft}^2 \text{ (safe)}$$

CP7C

PROBLEM: To design the size of a square footing for a given load applied to a uniform soil

Data

A stanchion load of 40 tons is to be carried, at a depth of 10 ft below the surface, on a square footing. The soil has a bulk density of 100 lb/ft^2 and an apparent cohesion of 250 lb/ft^2. The angle of shearing resistance is measured as 10°. Factor of safety to be used, 3.

Result required

The length of the side of the square footing to give a safe bearing capacity.

Method of attack

(1) The whole of the Terzaghi equation is required. Substitute the known values:

$$q = 1 \cdot 3 \times 250 \, N_c + 100 \times 10 \times N_q + 0 \cdot 4 \times 100 \, BN_\gamma.$$

(2) From the graph of bearing capacity factors find $N_c = 10$, $N_q = 4$, $N_\gamma = 2$ and substitute:

$$q = 3250 + 4000 + 80 \, B.$$

(3) This gives the value of the ultimate bearing capacity which is also equal to the load divided by the area of the footing. Therefore q also equals $(40 \times 2240)/B^2$ and $(40 \times 2240)/B^2 = 7250 + 80 \, B$.

(4) Solving this equation by trial and error, Table CP7C is

Table CP7C

(1) Dimension of square footing B (ft)	(2) B²	(3) 7·25 B² (in thousands)	(4) 10·80 B² (in thousands)	(5) B³	(6) 0·08 B³ (in thousands)	(7) (3) + (6) First solution (Terzaghi)	(8) (4) + (6) Second solution (Meyerhof)
2	4	29	43	8	1	30	44
3	9	65	97	27	2	67	99
4	16	116	173	64	5	121	178
5	25	181	270	125	10	191	280

constructed, and Fig. CP7C drawn. When $W = 7250 B^2 + 80 B^3$ is equal to $89 \cdot 6 \times 10^3$ the footing is on the point of failure.

(5) To bring the size to a safe dimension it is necessary to divide the ultimate bearing pressure by three, or multiply the area of the footing by three. The area of footing which gives a safe bearing capacity is thus a square of side $\sqrt{3 \cdot 5^2 \times 3} = 5 \cdot 7$ feet square or a safe bearing pressure of $1 \cdot 2$ ton/ft^2.

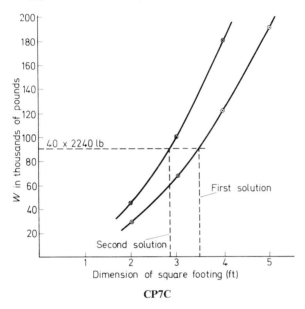

CP7C

(6) Strictly speaking this solution is not correct, for the Terzaghi expression is intended for shallow footings only, for those where the depth is not greater than the width of the footing. Meyerhof has produced graphs of bearing capacity coefficients for deep footings, and these can now be applied by referring to Fig. 7.5.

(7) Meyerhof's deep footings are strip footings, but an estimate could be made by using the Terzaghi equation for a square footing and applying Meyerhof's bearing capacity factors. For $\phi = 10°$ Meyerhof gives $N_c = 20$, $N_q = 4 \cdot 3$, $N_\gamma = 2$.

(8) With these expressions of a greater confidence in deep footings we have:

$$\frac{896 \times 10^3}{B^2} = 1\cdot3 \times 250 \times N_c + 100 \times 10 \times N_q + 0\cdot4 \times 100\ BN_\gamma,$$

$$W = 89\cdot6 \times 10^3 = 10{,}800\ B^2 + 80\ B^3.$$

(8) When this is solved on Fig. CP7C the difference between the "incorrect" Terzaghi solution and Meyerhof's is small. The size of the footing for ultimate failure is 2·8 feet square, and the size which would give a factor of safety against collapse of 3 would be $\sqrt{2\cdot8^2 \times 3}$ = 4·9 ft, or a safe bearing capacity of 1·7 ton/ft².

(9) Such a load should be checked for possible consolidation settlement, and it might be found that a much wider footing was needed to keep differential settlement to an acceptable level.

(10) It is to be noted in this calculation that extreme attention to detail is not necessary. There is no advantage in working to close limits, and the nearest 1000 in the terms of the equations was found to be quite adequate. Closer working would have made little difference.

CP7D

PROBLEM: To compare the ultimate bearing capacity of a strip footing as developed by Terzaghi and by Meyerhof

Data

     The footing is a strip with a width of 4 feet. The soil has an apparent cohesion of 80 lb/ft² and an angle of shearing resistance of 25°. Its bulk density is 110 lb/ft³. The footing is at a depth of 3 ft. Factor of safety to be used, 4.

Results required

     The safe bearing capacity of the foundation as estimated (a) by Terzaghi and (b) by Meyerhof.

Method of attack

     (1) The curves to use are shown in Fig. 7.4. The bearing capacity factors are (for 25°):

Terzaghi	$N_c = 25$:	$N_q = 13\cdot2$:	$N_\gamma = 10$
Meyerhof	$N_c = 20$:	$N_q = 11\cdot5$:	$N_\gamma = 6\cdot5$

(2) Substituting, we have:

Terzaghi
$$q = cN_c + \gamma z N_q + 0.5\,\gamma B N_\gamma$$
$$= 80 \times 25 + 110 \times 3 \times 13.2 + 0.5 \times 110 \times 4 \times 10$$
$$= 7760\ \text{lb/ft}^2.$$

Meyerhof
$$q = cN_c + \gamma z N_q + 0.5\,\gamma B N_\gamma$$
$$= 80 \times 20 + 110 \times 3 \times 11.5 + 0.5 \times 110 \times 4 \times 6.5$$
$$= 6830\ \text{lb/ft}^2.$$

(3) The safe bearing capacities are one-quarter of these, or 1940 lb/ft^2 and 1710 lb/ft^2 (0.87 and 0.76 ton/ft^2). Add 3×110 lb/ft^2.

CP7E

PROBLEM: To compare the values of ultimate bearing capacity for a square footing on the surface, as assessed by various authorities

Data

The footing is 6 ft square and rests on the surface. The soil has a cohesion of 250 lb/ft^2 and an angle of shearing resistance of 15°. Its weight is 109 lb/ft^3.

Results required

Assessment of the ultimate bearing capacity by (a) Terzaghi, (b) Meyerhof and (c) Skempton.

Method of attack

(1) By substitution of values in the Terzaghi equation, using Fig. 7.4 for strip footings and the coefficients for a square footing (Section 7.7), the ultimate bearing capacity is:

$$q = 1.3\,cN_c + \gamma z N_q + 0.4\,\gamma B N_\gamma$$
$$= 1.3 \times 250\ N_c + 109 \times \text{zero}\ N_q + 0.4\ 109 \times 6 \times N_\gamma$$
$$= 325 \times 13 + 153 \times 2.5 = 4610\ \text{lb/ft}^2.$$

(2) Using the Terzaghi equation for strip footings without alteration of the coefficients, but with the use of Meyerhof bearing factors (Fig. 7.6), the result is:

$$q = cN_c + \gamma z N_q + 0.5\,\gamma BN_\gamma$$
$$= 250 \times 15\tfrac{1}{2} + \text{Zero} + 0.5 \times 109 \times 6 \times 1.2$$
$$= 3875 + 174 = 4050\ \text{lb/ft}^2.$$

(3) Skempton's expression for the coefficient to be applied to a bearing capacity for strip loading is given in Section 7.7.

$$q = 1.2\,\{cN_c + \gamma z N_q + 0.5\,\gamma BN_\gamma\}$$
$$= 1.2\,\{250 \times 13 + 0.5 \times 109 \times 6 \times 2.5\}$$
$$= 1.2 \times 3425 = 4110\ \text{lb/ft}^2.$$

CP7F

PROBLEM: To determine the ultimate bearing capacity of a sandy gravel from the results of a standard penetration test

Data

The bed of sandy gravel was found to offer a resistance to the standard penetration test of 16 blows. The density of the material is 104 lb/ft³ and the breadth of the footing, 5 ft. Depth of footing below surface: 3 ft.

Result required

A possible range of values within which the ultimate bearing capacity is likely to lie.

Method of attack

(1) The angle of shearing resistance lies between 35° and 40°, probably somewhere midway between these two values (see Table 7A).

(2) From Fig. 7.4, N_q is approximately 60 and N_γ is also about 60. This is for a shallow foundation (3 ft deep).

(3) For a deeper foundation, Fig. 7.5 can be used, where the same bearing capacity factors have values of approximately 500 for both N_q and N_γ. Even these values can be larger, depending on the depth of the footing. For a granular soil, the figures just given refer to a ratio of depth to breadth of about 10.

(4) Evaluating, we have, for a shallow footing,

$$q = 104 \times 3 \times 60 + 0{\cdot}5 \times 104 \times 5 \times 60 = 34{,}300 \text{ lb/ft}^2$$
$$= 15{\cdot}3 \text{ ton/ft}^2,$$

and for a deep footing,

$$q = 104 \times 3 \times 500 + 0{\cdot}5 \times 104 \times 5 \times 500 = 129 \text{ ton/ft}^2.$$

It can be appreciated how much higher these are than the values obtained for $c - \phi$ soils and for cohesive soils.

Chapter 8

Limitation of Settlement

8.1. Structural Damage due to Settlement

The object of this chapter is to give guidance to the architect on the causes of settlement of buildings, and to point the way to the design of foundations aimed at avoiding structural damage due to settlement. It is assumed that the chapters of Parts I and II have been studied and understood. Terms, properties and methods of calculation discussed in the first six chapters are used in this present chapter without further explanation. If the methods of investigating possible settlement, as described here, are not understood, the reason may lie in an inadequate study of earlier chapters. Revision is recommended.

The average value of settlement over the whole area of a building, and the individual settlements suffered by different parts of it, govern the degree to which the building fulfils its purpose. The intensity of damage done to the structure by its settlement can range from complete functional failure to slight disfigurement of the plaster finishes. The architect must decide what degree of settlement can be permitted. He can then make some estimate of how movement of the foundation may be limited to this range.

Such estimation and planning is not simple, but an understanding of the principles which govern settlement, and of the types of soil and types of building most susceptible to movement, makes the estimation more logical and more likely to be of the right order. The final figures predicted can never be expected to agree precisely with those obtained later by direct measurement. A discrepancy of 10% to 20% between calculated and observed settlement represents an acceptable standard of prediction, and the discrepancy can be greater.

The amount and distribution of settlement over a building foundation depend not only on the properties of the soil strata on the site, but also on the degree of rigidity or of flexibility of the building concerned. The more compressible the soil, the greater will be the total settlement; the more flexible the structure of the building, the greater the likelihood of differential settlement. Conditions may be combined in many ways to attempt to meet a defined measure of allowable structural damage.

The definition of what constitutes structural damage must vary as the type of building changes. If, with unimpaired ability to carry out its purpose, a building can suffer a degree of structural distortion, the architect need not increase the cost of the building by measures to decrease that distortion. Differential settlement distorts a structure, but equal distortions may cause very different degrees of damage, depending on the design of the frame or load-bearing walls, and on the types and methods of cladding. Several inches of settlement of a single-storey warehouse building may not be noticed, but a slight movement may cause unacceptable cracking in decorative finishes. Even now, all the relationships existing between average settlement, maximum settlement, differential settlement, type of building, type of infilling, shape and size of foundations and the degrees of structural damage have not been defined, because of the lack of documented cases. It would be of great value if architects could keep logs of settlement of their buildings, and of any damage suffered. These details, related through the primary site investigation to the calculated theoretical settlement, would do a great deal to make even more reliable the predictions of settlement which are already possible.

8.2. Progress of Settlement

Settlement may be caused by complete or partial withdrawal of support, as in undermining by coal, salt or ironstone mines, or by the movement of soil in a mass, as in a slip. The subject of this chapter, however, is the more normal phenomenon—a reduction in the volume of the soil caused by the superimposed weight of a building, or by a change in moisture content from some other cause. Reduction in volume of the soil occurs when there is a decrease in the void ratio; the volume of solid particles always remains unchanged. The ultimate result is a decrease in volume of the supporting soil. The movement of the soil laterally is generally insignificant (unless due to mining subsidence) and the major effect on a building is a vertical downward movement. A study of the mechanism of this movement makes clear some important factors which illuminate the reasons for settlement and for the different types of settlement encountered.

Foundations on granular soils present little difficulty. First, void ratios for granular soils are low and, even if particles do move closer together, the reduction in volume cannot be large so long as the soil is contained and the only disturbing force is the weight of the building. Terzaghi, who had very wide experience, once stated that of all the buildings he knew to be founded on sand, none settled more than three inches. Secondly, downward movement of particles of sand is usually rapid. The grains of sand or gravel can almost be said to move immediately into the void spaces under pressure from the building erection. Thirdly, any settlement likely to take place keeps pace with construction (Fig. 8.1). The greatest settlement occurs during the erection of the building and, by the time the finishes are being applied, there is little fear of further movement if the foundation is on purely granular material.

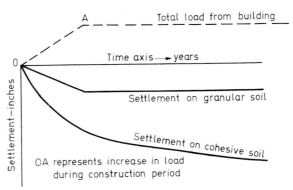

Fig. 8.1. Settlement of building on granular and cohesive soils.

One qualification is needed to this statement. The ground-water conditions must not be altered. Settlement of buildings on granular soils has occurred, sometimes with costly consequences, when pumping (from water-bearing strata under the building) has been commenced after the building was completed. By the lowering of the water-table near and underneath the building, the pore-pressure was reduced over some depth and area, and the effective pressure increased. An increase in effective pressure, by whatever means it is caused, has the same effect in reducing the void ratio and the volume as does the application of the weight of a heavy building. Settlement must ensue whether the reduction in volume is caused by construction loads or by the abstraction of water. To allow the latter after the construction load has been applied is dangerous

Most buildings, especially in temperate zones, rest eventually on saturated soil, and reduction in void ratio cannot occur until some water leaves the soil. Cohesive soils, because of their relatively low permeability, settle slowly; it is difficult to drive water out of them. The applied pressure or nett loading intensity in such soils is first carried by the water in the voids and is only gradually transferred from the water to the particles of the soil as the excess pore pressure is dissipated. This requires, for clay, a long period of continuing pressure. As the pore pressure caused by the superload decreases, after the passage of time, the particles move into closer packing and settlement takes place.

The difference between the behaviour of granular and cohesive soils lies in the timing. In contrast with the effects noted for granular soils, when settlement is immediate, only a small proportion of the final settlement has taken place by the time that a building on a clay foundation is completed (Fig. 8.1). For years thereafter, the building settles at a rate becoming gradually slower until the movement, although still taking place, makes no difference to such structural damage as has been suffered. The architect must decide how much of the total possible settlement is likely to be significant, and adjust his design to ensure that this settlement will produce no more than the permitted amount of structural damage.

Many of the cracks seen in buildings on clay are due to a faulty relationship between design features of substructure and super-structure, and the magnitudes and distribution of the settlements induced by these features. To avoid such cracking in his building, the architect must be familiar with how settlement occurs in simplified conditions. Then, by studying how the more complex conditions applied by buildings can modify the simpler results, he can design logically and avoid the cracking, so often unexpected by the architect, but as often inevitable if conditions of design are not successfully adapted to the characteristics of the soil.

8.3. Prediction of Settlement

When an excavation is made in preparation for the construction of a foundation, there is a release of pressure because of the removal of the weight of soil. This may cause a rise or swelling of the soil at the bottom of the excavation. The construction, in its first stages, restores this to some extent and the soil tends to return to its original volume. During this period, some of the settlement is elastic. As the construction proceeds and the load increases in value, consolidation settlement begins to take place according to the properties of the soil and its behaviour under stress (Chapters 2 and 5). It is this consolidation settlement which is the subject of the work in this present chapter.

If planning to avoid excessive settlement is to be effective, it is necessary to be able to predict the likely value of the final settlement. It is also important to know if this prediction is likely to agree with the value of the settlement finally measured after the building is completed. MacDonald and Skempton have made some important studies of settlement, comparing the predicted settlement of large buildings with that actually suffered. They found that the method of measuring consolidation as given in Chapter 5, and of applying this to the prediction of settlement of buildings, has been surprisingly accurate. On the results of 20 cases, the ratio of calculated to observed settlements had an average value of 1·05. This level (within 5%) of accuracy of prediction of final nett settlement certainly confirms the reliability of the method of calculation used (see Chapter 5).

8.4. Allowable Settlement

It is useful to know that the prediction of final settlement can be made with acceptable accuracy, but this does not assist in deciding on how much settlement should be allowed for a particular type of building. There is no way by which permissible settlement can be calculated. The decision must be based on empirical assessment of damage suffered by buildings where settlements have been measured and recorded.

The first point worth making is that the value of the maximum settlement likely to be suffered by the building does not constitute a valid criterion of whether structural damage will ensue. In one school, studied by the author's university department, the settlement was more than two feet (due in this instance to mining subsidence) but there was no visible damage. This was due to the matching of construction and design to the possibility of large-scale settlement; neither teachers nor pupils realized that settlement had taken place. In one technical study of this problem, a building was described which had settled only one-quarter of an inch at one end, but 21 inches at the other. It had rotated uniformly, and, apart from a few small cracks, was undamaged and continued to be occupied. On the other hand, where design had not been matched to possible movement, a mere two-inch maximum settlement was enough to disrupt and damage another structure so badly that it had to be demolished and rebuilt. Naturally, large settlements are always inconvenient and may cause serious disturbance of services even if no structural damage to the building itself is evident. Large settlements could not be tolerated, for example, in telephone exchanges where the links between inside and outside of the building are important. The magnitude of the maximum settlement, however, is no measure of the ability of the building to carry out its functions.

What is of very much greater importance than the maximum settlement is the differential settlement. If one part of the building settles more than another, the resulting racking or twisting is destructive. Naturally, such differential settlement has a more noticeable effect if the two points at which the settlement is measured are close together. If, for example, the settlements are measured at adjacent columns, the shearing effect on the building frame and on the panel in-filling can be assessed. This shear is measured by the angular distortion which occurs between stanchions which settle through different amounts. The slopes can be given as gradients—d in L (Fig. 8.2).

Skempton and MacDonald, in their studies of settlement, again compared the records of buildings which had suffered damage through settlement. This time they were able to find records of 98 buildings of varying types having either load-bearing walls, or steel or concrete frames. For these types they found a distinct change in the pattern of damage when the angular distortion $(d:L)$ reaches $1:300$. Buildings which show a steeper angular racking than this have been invariably damaged by cracks in the cladding. Buildings showing a flatter shear angle are undamaged. The frames of the buildings studied (as distinct from their cladding and finishes) showed no distress until the angular distortion was 1:150.

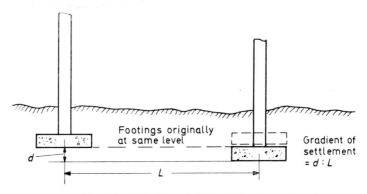

Fig. 8.2. Definition of differential settlement.

Skempton and MacDonald also found a good correlation between maximum settlement and maximum angular distortion. It is certainly possible that a building having a large maximum settlement will be more likely to have a large differential settlement, but this relationship is by no means always found to be true. Large settlements should be avoided, but large settlements do not inevitably cause damage whereas large angular distortions do. The rate at which movement takes place also has a bearing on the amount of damage suffered. Movements which would cause cracking if applied relatively rapidly, as by underpinning, do not necessarily cause damage if they occur naturally to the same extent over a number of years.

It is not always necessary to eliminate differential settlement altogether. On a clay soil many years may pass before settlement, and therefore differential settlement, reaches a value sufficient to cause cracking in the cladding or in the members of the frame. It would be uneconomical to provide foundations which would show no appreciable settlement after 30 or 40 years in order to avoid the necessity of making repairs in the panels after that length of time. It is thus very often more efficient, and more equitable for the client, to accept the fact that some differential settlement will take place, and to allow for repairs and maintenance.

8.5. Avoidance of Differential Settlement

It should be realized that the criteria of 1 : 300 for infilling panels and 1 : 150 for frames are only rough guides to the angular distortion to be looked upon as critical. Other factors come into the picture. The general routine of study for buildings on compressible soils, however, should be to determine the maximum likely settlement under the building assuming it to be supported on separate footings or on a very flexible raft. If this notional maximum settlement does not exceed $2\frac{1}{2}$ to 3 inches, it is likely that differential settlement of a uniform soil will be small, and that no further investigation is needed. However, in such an important matter, it is likely that the architect will want to make a further and more detailed investigation of the settlements of the various parts of the building in order to assess the maximum angular distortion likely to be suffered. The first rule in avoiding damaging differential settlement is thus to keep the maximum settlement of the building small. But more than this can be done.

On a uniform soil, absolute uniformity of loading over the whole surface does not produce uniform settlement over the whole area. The settlement which occurs is greater in the centre of the building and can only be called "dish-shaped". The bottom of an oil tank filled with liquid and resting on a flexible base settles in this way. A pattern of isolated footings carrying equal loads from equally spaced footings at the same level in uniform soil has the same effect. The columns nearer the centre, because of interaction of stresses in the soil, settle more than the columns towards the edges. Techniques of unequal loading can, therefore, bring the reward of a much more uniform settlement. This is an example of matching design and construction to the expected movement of the building. The loading of the outer stanchions with heavier loads, the spacing of the interior stanchions more widely, or the construction of a basement in the centre to relieve the original pressure on the ground and so allow a greater nett loading intensity, are all methods of avoiding the damage which might result from differential settlement.

The converse of these measures and others like them increases the danger of differential settlement. The building of a basement at one end of the building and not at the other, the closer spacing of equally loaded columns in the centre of the building, the lighter loading of stanchions towards the outer edges, may all have claims to be allowed because of functional requirements, but it must be remembered that on a cohesive soil, such measures invite angular distortion, and no architect should be surprised when cracking occurs.

Unequal loading of a uniform soil can be caused by founding the stanchions at different depths, or by carrying stanchions on piles which have not been driven to equal depths but merely to refusal. The application of load in this way at different heights above the base of a compressible stratum causes different values of consolidation to occur, and differential settlement of equally loaded stanchions to become evident. Differential settlement can also be encouraged by varying the volume of soil stressed by the foundation. Separate footings more heavily loaded may still enclose a smaller and shallower amount of soil than a wide raft foundation even if it is very lightly loaded. If the larger bulb of pressure intersects a deep-lying soft stratum, the differential settlement on the raft may be greater than is shown by the individual stanchions. If the raft is properly constructed to take bending moment and remain rigid, damage may not ensue even if the differential settlement on different parts of the raft is measurable. Many so-called "rafts" are, however, merely thicker floors and have little or no resistance to the stresses caused by movement.

8.6. Value of Maximum Settlement

In the study of settlement on a particular stratum or on a site where there are various strata underlying each other, the basic figure which must first be determined is the maximum settlement likely to be suffered, eventually, by any part of the building. Sometimes this is caused by the pressure applied by overlapping bulbs of pressure from adjacent footings. Sometimes it is the result of the placing of a footing where settlement is affected by a soft layer of material having a high coefficient of compressibility. It is not difficult to decide, after a little experience, the few points in a building where the maximum settlement might possibly occur.

The settlement of an individual foundation pad can be calculated from the measured conditions, such as are illustrated in the computation panels. The relief of pressure induced by the excavation of the depth of soil for the insertion of the footing should always be allowed. This value of bulk density multiplied by the depth is kept in reserve as an extra allowance after the allowable bearing pressure is calculated.

If the intensity of loading applied through the footing pad is p, then the nett loading intensity is $p - \gamma z$. This nett loading intensity results in vertical stresses in the various layers underlying the foundation according to the methods described in Chapter 4. The properties of the materials underlying the footings have presumably been studied, and the relevant coefficient of compressibility determined for various pressures. An example of this variation of the coefficient of compressibility is given in Fig. CP5D, for example.

The settlement of each stratum of soil is obtained by multiplying together the average vertical pressure, the thickness of the stratum and the relevant coefficient of compressibility. Examples of the use of this technique are given in the computation panels.

Final settlement $= m_v t p$ (length).

8.7. Rate of Settlement

The study of the rate of settlement under the footings of a building follows the method described in Chapter 5. There, the study was of samples of soil so thin that the total settlement likely to occur could be induced in a short time. Under the building, the final settlement calculated as in the last section from the coefficient of compressibility may take many years. The rate at which the first half of that settlement may take place is of some interest, for it is during this period that any damage likely to occur will show itself. Again, this somewhat complex calculation is better shown by example. The reader is referred to the computation panels of this chapter.

From the possible total settlement, from the rate at which various degrees of consolidation appear, from the distance apart of stanchions and from the type of building to be supported, the architect can decide on the possibility of structural damage and whether the design of the building should be varied.

COMPUTATION PANELS EIGHT

Prerequisite reading: Chapter 8 and Sections 3.2, 5.7, 5.10

Reminders
Difference in settlement of two adjacent stanchions: d (length)
Distance between stanchions for purpose of recording gradient of differential settlement: L
Suggested maximum distortion to avoid damage to finishes:
$d:L = 1:300$
Suggested maximum distortion to avoid damage to structural frames:
$d:L = 1:150$

Rate of settlement: $t = \dfrac{T_v d^2}{c_v}$

See also Reminders for Computation Panels Five.

CP8A

PROBLEM: To estimate the final settlement of a strip footing due to the consolidation of a clay layer

Data
   The strip footing is 4 ft wide and carries a load of 2 ton/ft². It is based at 3 ft below ground level in a soil with a bulk density of 102 lb/ft³. A stratum of clay lies between 8 ft 6 in and 13 ft 6 in below the ground surface. Figure CP8A shows the variation of the coefficient of compressibility for this clay for various nett loading intensities.

Result required
   The probable settlement of the footing when all movement has ceased.

Method of attack
   (1) Draw the conditions as in Fig. CP8A. It is always advisable to make sketches of this kind.

(2) Using Table 4B determine the influence factor for vertical stress at the mean point in the clay stratum. The sketch of the distribution of pressure (also from Table 4B) shows that the mean pressure on the line CL can be taken to refer to the whole thickness if only an approximate estimate of ultimate settlement is required. The value of the influence factor for B/z of $4/8$ (0.5) is 0.306. The excess stress imposed by the loading is, therefore, 2 ton/ft^2 × 0.306 = 0.612 ton/ft^2.

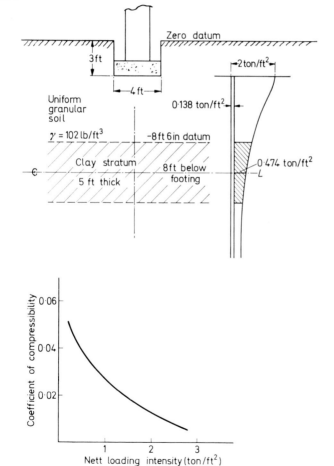

CP8A

(3) But the whole of the soil below the footing has been relieved of an original load by the excavation of the 3 ft. The nett loading intensity is thus reduced by 3×102 lb/ft^2 or 0·138 ton/ft^2. The final nett loading intensity is thus $0·612 - 0·138 = 0·474$ ton/ft^2.

(4) From the graph, the coefficient of compressibility for this intensity of loading is 0·041. Thus:

Settlement $= m_v tp = 0·041 \times 5 \times 0·474 = 0·097$ ft $= 1·2$ inches.

CP8B

PROBLEM: To compare the settlement of the corner and the centre of a flexible square footing

Data

It is proposed to erect a temporary tank to hold 10 ft of water. The base of the tank is to be flexible, and probably made of a polythene sheet. The tank is to be 12 ft square. It will rest on a deep clay stratum the performance of which in a consolidation test is shown in Fig. CP8B. Its bulk density is 100 lb/ft^2.

Results required

(a) The settlement in inches of the corner of the tank.
(b) The settlement in inches of the centre of the floor.

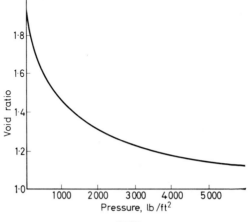

CP8B

Table CP8B/1

(1)	(2)	(3)	(4)	(5)	(6)	B = 6 ft (7)	Corner (8)	(9)	(10)	Centre (11)	(12)
Stratum no.	Depth z (ft)	Pressure before consolidation (soil) (lb/ft²)	V.R. for original condition	$\frac{B}{z}$	Influence factor (Table 4C)	Pressure due to load (lb/ft²)	Combined effective pressure (lb/ft²)	V.R. for combined pressure	Pressure due to load (lb/ft²)	Combined effective pressure (lb/ft²)	V.R. for combined pressure
A	0	0	1·92	∞	0·2500	175	175	1·78	700	700	1·52
B	3	300	1·70	2·0	0·2325	163	463	1·62	652	952	1·48
C	6	600	1·56	1·0	0·1752	123	723	1·52	492	1092	1·44
D	12	1200	1·42	0·5	0·0840	59	1259	1·42	236	1436	1·38
E	15	1500	1·38	0·4	0·0602	46	1546	1·36	184	1684	1·34
	30	3000	1·24	0·2	0·0179	13	3013	1·24	52	3052	1·24

Method of attack

(1) It is possible, as in the last problem CP8A, to assume that over a thickness of clay conditions vary so uniformly that the mean condition is to be found at the centre of the layer. However, when the layer is thick, it is better to divide it into horizontal slices and study the settlement of each slice, adding the individual results to obtain the final settlement. The depth to be considered should be about twice the width of the footing or foundation.

(2) To a depth of 30 ft, the clay is divided into five layers of varying thickness. These layers are A, B, C, D and E. In Table CP8B/1 columns (3) and (4) define the original conditions of effective pressure and void ratio before the load is applied. In Table CP8B/2, column (13) shows the mean void ratio for each of the five layers.

(3) For a square of 12 ft side, it is convenient to consider the stress caused by a corner of a 6-ft square. From Table 4C, for various values of B/z ($B = 6$ ft) the influence factors can be obtained. These multiplied by the proposed loading of 700 lb/ft^2 (a little more than the weight of 10 ft of water), give the vertical stresses imposed at various levels in the soil (column (7)).

(4) At the centre of the 12-ft square, four corners of the 6-ft squares come together, and the stresses imposed at the centre can be found by multiplying column (7) by four. This gives column (10).

Table CP8B/2

Soil stratum	Mean void ratio for original ground	Corner		Centre		Settlement at a corner (ft)	Settlement in the centre (ft)
		Mean void ratio	Differ-ence from (13)	Mean void ratio	Differ-ence from (13)		
(1)	(13)	(14)	(15)	(16)	(17)	(18)	(19)
A	1·81	1·70	0·11	1·50	0·31	0·12	0·33
B	1·63	1·57	0·06	1·46	0·17	0·05	0·19
C	1·49	1·47	0·02	1·41	0·08	0·05	0·19
D	1·40	1·40	—	1·36	0·04	—	0·05
E	1·30	1·30	—	1·29	0·01	—	0·07
				Final consolidation		0·22 Corner	0·83 ft Centre

(5) Columns (7) and (10) are combined with column (3) to obtain the pressures at various depths after the tank is filled. These pressures are given in columns (8) and (11).

(6) From columns (8) and (11), by the use of Fig. CP8B, the void ratios for the final states at corner and centre can be read off (columns (9) and (12)).

(7) In Table CP8B/2 the centre points of each of the layers are considered, and the mean void ratios for the three conditions found. Before loading, the mean void ratio is shown in column (13), and after loading the mean void ratios at corner and centre are shown respectively in columns (14) and (16).

(8) The differences in void ratios caused by the loading are given by (13) − (14) and (13) − (16), and these differences are used to determine the consolidation of each layer.

(9) The consolidation of each layer is found by the following relationship:

$$\frac{\text{Difference in void ratio} \times \text{thickness of layer}}{\text{One plus the original void ratio (13)}}.$$

These figures are given in columns (18) and (19), and the expected "dish-shaped" settlement appears, for the centre deflects under the consolidation by nearly four times the movement of the corner. A rigid slab, which cannot adjust itself to the uneven settlement caused by uniform loading, must suffer stresses due to bending. In this instance the base merely follows the settlement.

PROBLEM: To estimate the settlement caused by lowering of the water table

Data
A school stands on a deep stratum of sand (40 ft thick). Beneath this lies a layer of clay 20 ft thick, and below this is a horizontal surface of impervious rock. The sand has an average void ratio of 0·7. The water table is horizontal and lies at 6 ft below the surface of the sand. Above the water table the average degree of saturation is 0·6.

Tests on the clay give the curve of void ratio against effective pressure, as shown (Fig. CP8C). The specific gravity for both clay and sand can be taken as 2·7. Bulk density of clay, 120 lb/ft³.

It is proposed to supply water to the school by pumping from the sand. It is estimated that the water table under the school will be drawn down by 13 ft if this scheme is carried out. A light school building is assumed, for the sake of simplicity. It applies an insignificant load.

Result required
The probable settlement of the school as a result of the pumping.

Method of attack
(1) There is no question here of pore pressures being dissipated as occurs when drainage of the expelled water takes place. In this instance pore pressure will always be present, and it is essential to work with effective pressures.

(2) The bulk density of the sand can be obtained from the mean void ratio:

$$\gamma = \frac{G_s + e}{1 + e}\gamma_w = \frac{2\cdot7 + 0\cdot7}{1\cdot7} \times 62\cdot4 = 125 \text{ lb/ft}^3.$$

The bulk density of the sand above the water table can be found from the void ratio and degree of saturation.

$$\gamma = \frac{G_s + se}{1 + e}\gamma_w = \frac{2\cdot7 + 0\cdot42}{1\cdot7} \times 62\cdot4 = 114 \text{ lb/ft}^3.$$

The bulk density of the clay is given as 120 lb/ft³.

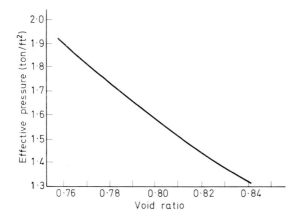

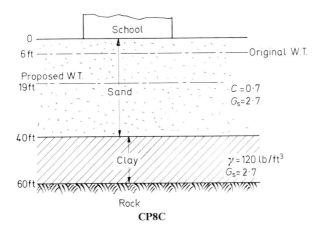

CP8C

(3) The total pressure at the centre of the clay layer is:

Total pressure $6 \times 114 + 34 \times 125 + 10 \times 120$
$= 684 + 4250 + 1200$
$= 6134$ lb/ft^2.

(4) From this must be subtracted the pore pressure at the centre of the clay layer. There is a depth of water in the soil equal to 50 ft less 6 ft or 44 ft above the centre of the clay layer. Pore pressure is thus $44 \times 62 \cdot 4 = 2746$ lb/ft^2.

(5) The effective pressure at the centre of the clay layer is thus $6134 - 2746 = 3388$ lb/ft^2 or 1·45 ton/ft^2.

(6) Assuming that the mean value at the centre of a 20 ft layer gives at least an approximation to the conditions in the clay, this effective pressure results in a void ratio of 0·818 as read from the graph obtained from tests on the material.

(7) When the water table is lowered to 19 ft (13 ft lower than before), there will be a depth of 13 ft of sand with a 60 % saturation as before which causes an extra effective pressure. Above the water table the whole weight of the soil with the water in suspension is transmitted as an effective pressure to the soil below the water table. Thus we have:

Effective pressure at centre of clay layer (50 ft, with W.T. at 19 ft):

$$19 \times 114 + 21 (125 - 62·4) + 10 (120 - 62·4)$$

which is 4057 lb/ft^2 or 1·80 ton/ft^2. This corresponds to a void ratio of 0·772.

(8) The above value can be obtained without doing the whole calculation again, merely by adding the extra effective pressure caused by lowering the water table by 13 ft. The effective pressure over this depth changes from $(125 - 62·4)$ per foot of depth to 114 per foot of depth, or a change of $51·4 \times 13$ lb/ft^2 of effective pressure (668 lb/ft^2). This, added to the previous effective pressure, gives the value already obtained of 1·80 ton/ft^2.

(9) The void ratio in the clay when equilibrium is established after pumping has commenced is obtained from the graph as 0·772, as in (6).

(10) The settlement likely to be experienced by the clay is given by

$$\frac{\text{Difference in void ratio}}{1 + \text{original void ratio}} \times \text{Depth} = \frac{0·818 - 0·772}{1 + 0·818} \times 20$$

$$= \frac{0·046}{1·818} \times 20 = 0·51 \text{ ft.}$$

The probable consolidation of the clay can, therefore, amount to more than 6 inches. Settlement of the sand stratum is unlikely to be significant, in comparison.

CP8D

PROBLEM: To estimate the differential settlement occurring between two adjacent stanchions

Data

In excavating for the stanchions shown in Fig. CP8D it was found that there was a lens of loose sand as shown by the dotted

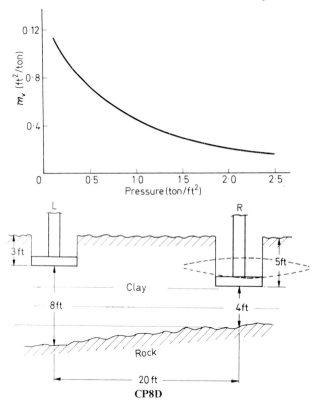

CP8D

lines. It was decided to found the stanchion R below this on the sound clay. The position of the rock was known, and stanchion L was founded (as originally intended for both stanchions) at 3 ft below the surface. The clay had a density of 110 lb/ft^3; on being tested in compression, it showed a coefficient of compressibility which varied with pressure as shown in the Fig. CP8D.

Result required

Some indication is required of the possibility of structural damage due to differential settlement, if the pressure applied by each footing is 2 ton/ft².

Method of attack

(1) The first step is to establish the original conditions before the stanchions were installed. Table CP8D/1 shows these original conditions as studied at five levels below the surface. At the mean pressures in each 2-ft layer, the value of the coefficient of compressibility is read off. Later, as the extra pressure is applied by the stanchions, the coefficient will decrease, but consolidation of the layer will start off, when pressure is applied, at the rate indicated by these original coefficients of compressibility.

Table CP8D/1

Original conditions

Depth from surface (ft)	Pressure due to weight of soil (lb/ft²)	(ton/ft²)	Mean pressure (ton/ft²)	m_v (ft²/ton) (from Fig. CP8D)
3	330	0·15		
			0·20	0·050
5	550	0·25		
			0·30	0·046
7	770	0·34		
			0·39	0·041
9	990	0·44		
			0·49	0·037
11	1210	0·54		

(2) One of the benefits of using the coefficient of compressibility instead of the void ratio in studying consolidation is that an elaborate analysis of original-plus-added conditions need not be made (see previous problems). Only the excess pressure applied at any layer need be calculated. Consolidation is then obtained from the coefficient of compressibility as found in Table CP8D/1.

(3) Up to column (5) in Table CP8D/2 the procedure follows the usual pattern as studied in Chapter 4. Using Table 4B or a graph

Table CP8D/2
Footing L

(1) Depth below surface z (ft)	(2) Depth below footing z (ft)	(3) B/z ($B = 5$ ft)	(4) Influence factor (Table 4B)	(5) I.F. $\times$ 2 ton/ft²	(6) Col. (5) less 0·15 ton/ft²	(7) Mean pressure (ton/ft²)	(8) m_v (ft²/ton) from Fig. CP8D	(9) Consolidation of layer (ft)
3	0	∞	1·00	2·00	1·85	1·73	0·050	0·173
5	2	2·50	0·88	1·76	1·61	1·38	0·046	0·126
7	4	1·25	0·65	1·30	1·15	0·97	0·041	0·080
9	6	0·83	0·47	0·94	0·79	0·70	0·037	0·052
11	8	0·63	0·38	0·76	0·61			
						Total settlement		0·431 ft

Table CP8D/3
Footing R

(10) Depth below surface (ft)	(11) Depth below footing z (ft)	(12) B/z ($B = 5$ ft)	(13) Influence factor (Table 4B)	(14) I.F. $\times$ 2 ton/ft²	(15) Col. (14) less 0·25 ton/ft²	(16) Mean pressure (ton/ft²)	(17) m_v (ft²/ton)	(18) Consolidation of layers (ft)
0								
3								
5	0	∞	1·00	2·00	1·75			
						1·63	0·046	0·150
7	2	2·50	0·88	1·76	1·51			
						1·28	0·041	0·105
9	4	1·25	0·65	1·30	1·05			
							Final settlement	$\overline{0·255}$ ft

prepared from it (which is probably more convenient) column (5) is completed showing the vertical pressures brought into play at various depths. This is the excess pressure applied to the soil in its original condition, except for the relief of load obtained by the excavation to a depth of 3 ft. Subtracting this value from the theoretical pressures, the nett loading intensity is recorded in column (6). A mean value for each of the 2-ft layers is then worked out.

(4) The final settlement is obtained by the following:

Mean nett effective pressure (column (6)) × coefficient of compressibility × the thickness of the layer.

For example, the layer between 5 ft and 7 ft from the surface has a consolidation of $1 \cdot 38 \times 0 \cdot 046 \times 2 \cdot 00 = 0 \cdot 126$ ft.

(5) In Table CP8D/3 a similar calculation is made for footing R. Naturally, this can hardly be an exact analysis with only two values in the calculation, but it is close enough to the truth (remembering all the uncertainties met and assumptions made) to give an indication whether the differential settlement will be damaging or not.

(6) Stanchion L settles ultimately by 0·43 foot. Stanchion R settles by only 0·26 foot. For stanchions 20 feet apart this represents a gradient of Differential settlement/Spacing of 0·17/20 or 0·0085 (1 in 120, approximately). The gradient allowed (or suggested as safe) is 1 in 300 or 0·0033. This situation (1:120) is, therefore, very likely to result in cracking of finishes and might even lead to more serious damage. The founding of stanchions with varying subsurface conditions is often necessary, but an investigation of differential settlement is worth making especially if the site investigation has supplied results of consolidation tests.

CP8E

PROBLEM: To determine the final settlement and rate of settlement of a raft due to the consolidation of two clay strata of different properties and drainage conditions

Data

A building on a 30 ft × 20 ft raft is founded on a dense sand layer, but there are two clay strata below, separated by a thin drainage layer of gravel. The conditions are given in Fig. CP8E and the results of consolidation tests on the clays are:

Clay stratum B:

$$m_{vb} = 0.037 \text{ ft}^2/\text{ton}: \quad c_{vb} = 3.4 \times 10^{-4} \text{ in}^2/\text{min}.$$

Clay stratum D:

$$m_{vd} = 0.028 \text{ ft}^2/\text{ton}; \quad c_{vd} = 4.2 \times 10^{-4} \text{ in}^2/\text{min}$$
$$(\text{in}^2/\text{min} = 3650 \text{ ft}^2/\text{year}).$$

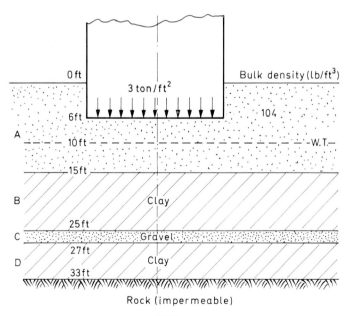

CP8E

Results required

(a) An estimate of the final settlement when both strata of clay have reached equilibrium under the load.

(b) The time likely to elapse before half of this settlement is produced.

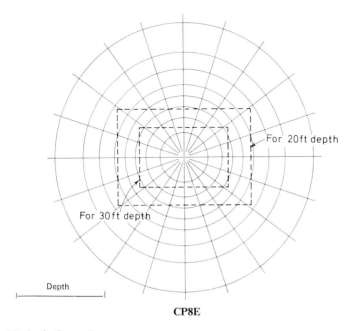

For 20 ft depth

For 30 ft depth

Depth

CP8E

Method of attack

(1) Since the coefficient of compressibility is given for each of the clay layers, only the nett loading intensity need be considered This is represented by the vertical pressure applied at the centre of each clay layer by the raft loading—relieved, of course, by the weight of 6 feet of sand which has been excavated to form the foundation.

The intensity of loading is obtained by using Newmark's Chart, Fig. CP8E. For the depth 20 ft, the rectangle to be drawn has a breadth equal to the line AB, and for the depth 30 ft, the rectangle has a length equal to the line AB. The method of using this chart is described in Chapter 4, and the technique should be familiar.

(2) The two rectangles are placed on the chart with the centres

of the rectangles at the centre of the chart and the number of spaces covered is counted. Each space represents an influence factor of 0·005.

Clay B: at 20 ft depth: 78 spaces:
$$\text{Pressure} = 78 \times 0·005 \times 3 = 1·17 \text{ ton/ft}^2.$$

Clay D: at 30 ft. depth: 48 spaces:
$$\text{Pressure} = 48 \times 0·005 \times 3 = 0·72 \text{ ton/ft}^2.$$

(3) The depth of soil excavated relieves both clay layers of a load per square foot equal to $104 \times 6 = 624$ lb/ft^2 or 0·28 ton/ft^2. The nett loading intensity at the centres of the two clay layers is, therefore,

$$\text{Clay } B: 1·17 - 0·28 = 0·89 \text{ ton/ft}^2$$
$$\text{Clay } D: 0·72 - 0·28 = 0·44 \text{ ton/ft}^2.$$

Since the figures obtained from the charts have been calculated on the assumption that the clay, sand and gravel in this foundation are all homogeneous and have the same properties in all directions, the accuracy cannot be high, but the order of stress values is probably reasonably correct, and gives some indication of conditions in the foundation material.

(4) The final settlement is obtained as follows: we assume that the sand and gravel do not consolidate significantly, and concentrate on the clay layers:

$$\begin{aligned}
\text{Final settlement} &= m_{vb}p_bH_b + m_{vd}p_dH_d \\
&= 0·37 \times 0·89 \times 10 + 0·28 \times 0·44 \times 6 \\
&= 0·33 + 0·074 \\
&= 0·40 \text{ ft, or 5 inches.}
\end{aligned}$$

(5) The determination of the *rate of settlement* is more complex. Since the B layer can drain in two directions, and the D layer only in one, and since the layers have different coefficients of consolidation, we can expect some difference in the degree of consolidation reached by the two layers at any given time. We cannot say that when the total settlement has reached the halfway point ($U = 0·5$) that the separate layers have also reached half their individual consolidations. The fact that the product of $c_{vb} \times m_{vb}$ is not very different from $c_{vd} \times m_{vd}$ shows that the coefficients of permeability of the two layers are

similar, and this may tend to cancel, to some extent, the other differences. We can only say:

$$U_{vb} \times \text{final settlement of B} + U_{vd} \times \text{final settlement of D}$$

must be equal to some degree of consolidation for the whole foundation multiplied by the final settlement of 0·4 ft.

Thus, for the halfway stage, $U = 0\cdot5$, and

$$U_{vb} \times 0\cdot33 + U_{vd} \times 0\cdot074 = 0\cdot5 \times 0\cdot40.$$

To reach any conclusion from this equation we must know at least the relationship between U_{vb} and U_{vd}.

(6) So long as the degree of consolidation is less than about 0·5, the relationships

$$U_{vb} = 1\cdot13 \sqrt{T_{vb}}$$

and

$$U_{vd} = 1\cdot13 \sqrt{T_{vd}}$$

hold good. Also, at any value of time since the loading of the foundation,

$$t = \frac{T_{vb}d_b{}^2}{c_{vb}} = \frac{T_{vd}d_d{}^2}{c_{vd}}.$$

Therefore,

$$\frac{T_{vb}}{T_{vd}} = \left(\frac{U_{vb}}{U_{vd}}\right)^2 = \frac{c_{vb}}{c_{vd}} \cdot \frac{d_d{}^2}{d_b{}^2}.$$

It follows that:

$$\frac{U_{vb}}{U_{vd}} = \sqrt{\frac{c_{vb}}{c_{vd}}} \times \frac{d_d}{d_b}.$$

If we substitute the values we know, a relationship between U_{vb} and U_{vd} can be obtained, provided the degree of consolidation is not more than 0·5. The values of d must be determined with care. The symbol d represents the longest drainage path through the clay layer. For the B layer, the path is 5 feet or one-half the thickness, for drainage is both upwards towards the sand, and downwards towards the gravel. For layer D, the drainage is in one direction only and the drainage path is equal to the thickness of the clay. Thus,

$$\frac{U_{vb}}{U_{vd}} = \sqrt{\frac{3\cdot4}{4\cdot2}} \times \frac{6}{5} = 1\cdot08.$$

Substituting in the expression in Section (5),

$$U_{vb} \times 0\cdot33 + U_{vd} \times 0\cdot074 = 0\cdot5 \times 0\cdot40$$
$$U_{vd} \times 1\cdot08 \times 0\cdot33 + U_{vd} \times 0\cdot074 = 0\cdot20$$
$$U_{vd} = 0\cdot47$$

but

$$U_{vb} = 1\cdot08 \times U_{vd} = 0\cdot51.$$

These are the degrees of consolidation of the two layers when the total consolidation of the whole foundation has reached the halfway mark.

(7) To determine how long this takes it is only necessary to substitute in the equation:

$$t = \frac{T_{vb} \times d_b{}^2}{c_{vb}} = \left(\frac{U_{vb}}{1\cdot13}\right)^2 \times \frac{5^2}{3\cdot4 \times 10^{-4}}$$

$$= \frac{0\cdot203 \times 25}{3\cdot4 \times 10^{-4} \times 3650} = 4\cdot1 \text{ years.}$$

It will take very much longer for the second half of the settlement to take place, since the curve flattens out.

CP8F

PROBLEM: To choose between two alternative systems of design for a foundation of a building when it is known that a soft clay layer underlies the site

Data

The building covers an area of 30 ft × 60 ft and carries a total load of 1800 tons. At a depth of 24 ft there is a soft clay layer of a few feet in thickness and which is likely to consolidate under the loading. The granular material which lies above and below the clay has a high shear strength and can take a safe bearing load of $2\frac{1}{2}$ ton/ft^2. The choice of foundation lies between three rows of six footings, each carrying 100 tons at $2\frac{1}{2}$ ton/ft^2 or a raft covering the whole site at 1 ton/ft^2. The second suggestion was made in order to reduce the pressure on the soil and so minimize the risk of the soft clay layer being affected.

Result required
A decision on which of the two systems is the more suitable in the circumstances.

Method of attack
(1) The magnitude of the risk of settlement can be determined by finding the value of the stress applied to the clay layer under the centre of the site.

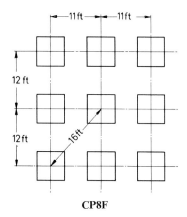

CP8F

(2) The value of the vertical stress at 24 ft depth under the centre of a rectangular foundation carrying 1 ton/ft^2, and measuring 60 ft × 30 ft, can be determined by the use of Newmark's charts or by Table 4C. The two methods agree well, the value of the stress at the point concerned being in the region of 0·6 ton/ft^2.

(3) As an approximation, the individual footings may be considered as point loads, and Table 4A used. Figure CP8F shows the dimensions concerned. We wish to determine the vertical stress imposed by the nine footings of Fig. CP8F at a point 24 ft below the central footing. Four of the footings lie at a radial distance of 16ft

from the centre, two at a radius of 12 ft and two at a radius of 11 ft. The methods of Section 4.5 (Fig. 4.1, Table 4A) are relevant.

(4) The values of r/z are zero, 0·67, 0·50 and 0·46, and the influence factors relating to these, from a graph drawn from Table 4A, or from a more extended version of the table, are, respectively, 0·48, 0·19, 0·27 and 0·31.

(5) The pressure required is thus:

$$\text{Vertical pressure} = \frac{100\ \text{ton}}{24^2}(0\cdot48 + 4 \times 0\cdot19 + 2 \times 0\cdot27 + 2 \times 0\cdot31)$$

$$= 0\cdot4\ \text{ton/ft}^2\ \text{(approximately)}$$

which is *less* than in (2) above.

(6) This example shows how the greater depth of the bulb of pressure under a wide foundation may have a more serious effect than a number of bulbs of pressure under individual foundations at much higher loading intensities. This is particularly true if the soft layer, likely to consolidate, lies at some depth below the surface. The conventional idea that to "spread the load" inevitably and invariably results in lower soil stresses should always be questioned. A quick check does not take long and may give enough indication of possible structural damage to permit of a redesign of the foundation arrangements.

Chapter 9

Allowable Bearing Pressure

9.1. Range of Soil Properties

The earlier chapters have shown how, even for the relatively few parameters chosen for study in this volume, the architect is faced with an enormously long range of soil properties. These must be used in calculation, according to the state of knowledge as it stands today, to determine the ultimate conditions which would tend to cause destruction of the building.

For a catastrophic shear failure this is, at least, relatively easy, for this type of collapse is precise and occurs suddenly. It is not nearly so easy to decide what range of settlement can be considered to be destructive. The settlement induced varies in dimension with the location and size of the footings, with their depth and with their proximity to or distance from neighbouring footings. The pattern of stanchions in a building defines not only the maximum settlement, but also the differential settlement, which is usually more important than the value of the total settlement.

The soil which causes the greatest problem is, of course, the cohesive soil. The cohesion, the coefficient of permeability, the coefficient of compressibility and the coefficient of consolidation control and direct the ability of the soil to produce a resistance to the loads applied. This resistance must be developed without movement which would be deleterious to the finishes or the structure of the building. This is the problem which confronts the architect when he must decide on the allowable bearing pressure to be applied by a footing.

9.2. Factor of Safety

Faced with the multitudinous, variable quantities presented by a cohesive soil, and with the way in which it changes its properties with time and under load, the architect, in choosing his allowable bearing pressure, sometimes shows a nonchalance which is very remarkable. If he is familiar with the area, and with the soils previously encountered, his subjective judgement may be reliable, and he may have no need of a site investigation or a series of tests and calculations. If, however, he is on strange ground, then he would do well to look on the design of the foundation as something demanding his critical attention. A site investigation is of very little use if it is not understood, or the warnings implicit in its tables of figures go ignored. The author was recently asked to give an opinion on a severe and costly shear failure, which necessitated the rebuilding of part of a large structure. He found that two site investigations had been carried out, by different firms. Both carried explicit and implicit prophecies of a certain failure if the architect's original ideas were carried out. For eighteen months the figures had been available to show that collapse of the structure and its foundation would occur, but the building went on according to the drawings and great expense was incurred in putting the matter right.

There are thus two ways of deciding on the factor of safety, load factor or the factor covering unknown but likely variations from the known or measured properties of the soil. These are (a) to rely on local knowledge, either without tests or with very simple tests, and make a decision based largely on previous experience, or (b) to have a full investigation made so that all the aspects of the previous chapters can be applied with confidence. This latter course can be costly, and is probably economic only for the larger structures. It must be remembered, however, that even the smaller structures can show structural damage due to inadequate foundations, and that this also can be costly. In this chapter both these ways of deciding on allowable bearing pressure (or factor of safety multiplied by the damaging bearing pressure) are studied.

9.3. Allowable Bearing Pressure from Fully Detailed Site Investigations

As was pointed out in Chapter 6, a site investigation must not be a vague exploration, but must be specifically directed to the determination of defined properties of the soil at levels likely to be important in the type of structure to be erected. If well-spaced footings are to be used, the soil will probably not be highly stressed below a depth of about twice the width of the footing. An investigation to this depth cannot safely be used as a basis for a change of plan to a large raft foundation for the whole building, where the effect of the loading will go very much deeper. The figures obtained from the site borings and tests must relate to the possible type of foundation envisaged.

The full site investigation which provides values of the consolidation characteristics of the soil as well as of the shear strength must be analysed and used during the period of preliminary design of foundations if it is to have its full effect and provide full value. It may be that several alternative arrangements of foundations are possible. The first step is to decide the safe bearing capacity (see definition in Chapter 7 to be sure the meaning of this term is thoroughly understood). With this as a basis for further analysis, the foundations should be designed and then tested for possible amount and rate of settlement. This calculation is based on the consolidation characteristics of the soil which have been reported in the returns from the site exploration.

The foundations having been shown to be safe against sudden shear failure (Chapter 7), the second analysis gives valuable information on the possibility of differential settlement, and defines the amount likely to be encountered between various parts of the building. Usually, it is easy, from the general survey of the results of the tests carried out, to pin-point certain areas of the site and certain depths where difficulties are likely to be encountered. Special care can be taken at these locations and depths to ensure that calculations such as those in Chapters 7 and 8 are thorough and painstaking.

If it is found that the differential settlement between two stanchions is more than can be tolerated with the design of foundation first selected, two steps can be taken. The first is to rearrange stanchions so that a better pattern is apparent. It is pointed out in Chapter 8 that a uniform arrangement of stanchions on a uniform soil does not result in a uniform settlement, and Problem CP8B illustrates this. It may be necessary as a part of the rearrangement to relieve pressure by including a basement in the centre of the building if conditions indicate that this will assist towards a uniform settlement. It is better to spend time on rearrangement of subsurface design than to deal with differential settlement and cracking at a later date.

If the site investigation is used correctly it should first be decided where over the site the danger areas lie. These are areas where, from the values of *cohesion, angle of shearing resistance, coefficient of compressibility, density, moisture content, soil classification* and *limits of consistency*, there is a likelihood of difficulty arising. This study of the conditions prevailing must be done in three dimensions. The proposed type of foundation defines the approximate volume of soil which will be appreciably stressed. A knowledge of what proportions a bulb of pressure is likely to display, and a few quick sketches, will bring to light the third dimension—depth—which must also be explored.

The investigator tries to decide where there is a possibility of a shear failure with the proposed type of footing. He estimates where settlement is likely to be large, and makes special studies of these areas with a view to determining the extent to which *differential* settlement may be expected. He then decides on a value of bearing pressure which can be looked upon as being destructive. This value may well be different for each footing, or at least for groups of footings. Variability on a site in all three dimensions must be taken as the rule rather than the exception. Dividing by a factor of safety, he then has the allowable bearing pressure for each part of the foundation. For some footings, settlement may be the critical phenomenon, for others, the possibility of shear failure. The object is to make sure that, whatever the differences which appear in the required type of foundation for each part of the building, conditions of pressure are adjusted to develop uniform behaviour of the structure. Adjustments in design may appear necessary even at this late stage so that the aim of uniform behaviour can be achieved.

In addition to a study of each part of the foundation, an examination should be made of the whole. This particularly applies where a raft or buoyant foundation is used. Reduction in the nett loading intensity without altering the weight of the building can be achieved by relieving the soil of a part of the weight it carries originally. The excavation of basements allows, on the same site, of a higher factor of safety or of a taller building. As a very rough guide it can be said that the excavation of a basement allows of the addition of another four storeys to the building without extra stress on the soil. A double "lower ground floor" allows of eight more storeys or a very much reduced likelihood of settlement. The extra refinement of a basement of variable depth limits differential settlement. The first basement over the whole area is followed at a lower level by a second covering only the centre of the building. This greater release of load in the centre, with a smaller release round the perimeter of the building, permits of a uniform loading over the area without a dish-shaped settlement.

9.4. Rafts and Buoyant Foundations

In the author's experience, the function and design of a foundation raft is often very much misunderstood by architects. The name is commonly applied to any large area of concrete on which a building is erected, the assumption being that this raft "spreads the load" and so reduces the stresses in the foundation soil. Continuous foundation slabs can apply a uniform, or approximately uniform, contact pressure to the soil in two ways:

(a) The slab can be uniformly loaded over its whole surface, and be flexible enough to follow any settlement produced. This can apply only where truly uniform pressure is applied and where settlement and differential settlement of the base does not cause structural damage. Such conditions apply only for tanks containing liquid, and then presuppose liquid-tightness and absence of any serious weakness in the foundation soil.

(b) The slab can be sufficiently rigid to resist, with little or no movement, all the moments applied by the distribution of concentrated loads over its surface. In theory, the stress applied by the edges of a rigid raft is infinitely large. In fact, plastic failure of the soil round the edges has the effect of distributing the load reasonably well. It is common and sound practice to assume a uniform contact pressure in these conditions.

What must not be assumed is that the thin flexible slab of (a) can carry out the functions of the slab described in (b). The author has often been asked to investigate cracking in so-called "rafts" and found that the unwarranted assumption has been made that a slab is a raft. Before a raft can be assumed to transmit a uniform pressure to the ground, it must be designed to carry heavy and variable loading. There are, from the superstructure, the stanchion and ground floor loadings, and there is, from the soil, the uplift pore pressure if the raft is below the water table. These result in a heavy and costly design, usually requiring deep beams and a heavy slab.

The light construction used in slabs and basement floors shows a lack of appreciation in the designer of the forces at work. The author has waded in damp basements where walls weep and floors are cracked and under water, because uplift pressure was not understood. A raft must be designed as a floor upside-down carrying an upward pressure equal to the bearing pressure imposed by the building. Pore-pressure, causing uplift, is present and the raft is "supported" by the stanchions of the building. Such a raft has a heavier construction than any of the floors within the superstructure of the building, and must, in addition, be made watertight.

A *buoyant foundation, floating foundation, caisson foundation* or *box foundation* is merely a deep watertight raft. Its function is to reduce the nett loading intensity on the soil at a given level, first by relieving it of the weight of soil originally lying above that level, and then replacing the soil by a building of approximately the same weight or only slightly heavier. The nett result is that the soil is in the same conditions as before excavation commenced, and settlement is substantially reduced or eliminated. This foundation is not used as much as it might be, and, even where basements are inserted at the request of the client, the architect sometimes does not fully realize the problems he has solved by this step, or the problems which he has imposed on the design.

Structurally, buoyant foundations must be rigid and properly designed for the forces imposed. This can mean either abandoning the use of this space below ground level for the functional purposes of the building, or realizing that functional purposes must be subservient to the requirements of strength, rigidity and water-tightness. The real problems arise in the construction of a foundation of this kind. As excavation proceeds in the poor ground for which buoyant foundations are suitable, pressure is relieved at the bottom of the excavation. As is shown in Chapter 3, these conditions may cause heaving of the bottom. If this occurs and is held by the erection of the building, it is almost certain that a settlement equal, approximately, to the heave will take place. Settlement of this kind is to be avoided, of course, even if, later, no more occurs because of the light value of the nett loading intensity. It is best, therefore, to avoid, even in very bad ground, the construction of a fully buoyant foundation—one in which the nett loading intensity is zero. Some small positive loading intensity should be chosen so that the depth of excavation need not reach a level likely to cause heave.

9.5. Allowable Bearing Pressure from a Simpler Site Exploration

The somewhat elaborate studies and investigations necessary for a large and important building, or for one in poor ground, need not always be made. The work described in Sections 9.3 and 9.4 is essential if anxiety over the behaviour of the building is to be reduced to a minimum. However, in known local conditions, or where the soil properties are known to present few problems to the designer of the foundations, a simple site investigation demanding only the estimation of the more readily obtained values of soil properties is not only cheaper, but as effective if used with knowledge.

Too often, large sums are expended on full site investigations which are either not fully used or are quite unnecessary in the circumstances. A great deal can be learnt from the investigation of results obtained from buildings already constructed. If architects would collect and publish the results of site investigations, the designs adopted, and the behaviour of the buildings in later years, even more effective design procedures might well be brought to light. The number of documented cases is small.

Professor Skempton of Imperial College, London, has been assiduous, with his colleagues, in comparing and assessing results already noted and in drawing conclusions from them. Some of these conclusions are described in Chapter 7. In the necessary decision on allowable bearing pressure, he has also developed some interesting relationships. These were put forward at the Building Research Congress in London in 1951.

Briefly he has found that by multiplying together the *strength* of the soil (cohesion: load/length^2) and the *coefficient of compressibility* (length^2/load) he has obtained a useful dimensionless factor. To make the figure easier to handle, the reciprocal is used $(1/cm_v)$. The value of this factor varies from low figures for normally-consolidated clays (25–50) to higher figures (up to 200) for over-consolidated clays. This can, of course, be only approximate, for m_v varies with the pressure applied. The flair, judgement and intuition, mentioned in Chapter 1, are still required. Backed by knowledge of the techniques and principles accepted today, intuitive design, balanced by simple tests, can produce viable results, and Skempton's use of this new factor shows how decisions can be influenced and adapted to circumstances.

The factor $1/cm_v$ is used to determine a factor of safety from the value of the ultimate bearing capacity and from requirements for acceptable settlement. First, the breadth of the foundation must be estimated. This is needed, not only in the determination of ultimate bearing capacity, but also for assessing the order of settlement likely to be reached by various designs. A wide footing produces a deeper bulb of pressure, and, in clay (for which this discussion is valid), a greater mass of soil under pressure entails a greater settlement. The factor of safety against settlement should, therefore, be higher for a wider footing.

Secondly, a decision must be made on the maximum settlement to be allowed, assuming that to limit the maximum settlement is to limit the more damaging differential settlement. A single-storey factory building may show no signs of distress with a maximum settlement of any one stanchion of 6 inches, but perhaps one inch would be the maximum possible in a more finished building. Here, again, the architect must apply his knowledge and experience. Clearly the factor of safety if only one inch settlement is to be allowed must be greater than if 6 inches is permitted.

In Fig. 9.1 Skempton's figures are plotted on logarithmic paper to give a guide—and it can be only a guide—to the order of the factor of safety to be applied to the ultimate bearing capacity. If these factors of safety are used, the architect is, of course, making a number of assumptions, based, perhaps, on sound evidence, but still assumptions depending on a "norm" of behaviour of different types of clay. There is no explicit relationship between strength and settlement, but it is at least likely that the weaker the clay the greater the settlement to be expected. It is on this kind of argument that Fig. 9.1 is based.

The result of this approach is that, for smaller buildings or buildings on what is accepted as a "good" foundation, only the cohesive strength (the shear strength) of the clay need be known, together with some estimate of whether it is normally consolidated or overconsolidated. If the clay has been studied for its consolidation characteristics and the change in void ratio with pressure is known,

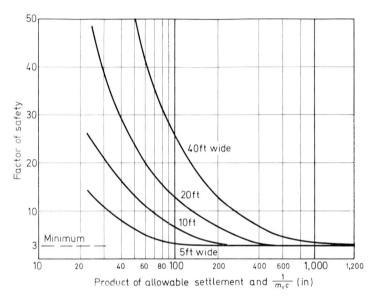

Fig. 9.1. Factors of safety.

some mean value of the coefficient of compressibility can be worked out without the more elaborate estimates required for a complete study of settlement. The value of the reciprocal of cm_v (which is dimensionless) is multiplied by the value of the maximum allowable settlement in inches. From Fig. 9.1 the factor of safety is then suggested. The minimum value used is 3. It is not advisable to use a smaller figure.

9.6. Final Design for the Foundation

Most of this book is concerned with analysis rather than with design, but the object, throughout, is to direct the architect to formulate designs based on knowledge as well as on intuitive and subjective assessment. To the young architect, lacking experience, these chapters can be a guide, so long as he does not become fascinated by the written calculation. Too often, figures worked out from uncertain assumptions, based on approximate values of properties and on an inadequate number of tests, come to hold an unjustified authority. To calculate bearing capacities to two decimal places is to show not "accuracy" but lack of judgement. Figures calculated by the techniques of this book are guides only. To be useful guides they must be numerous. Many tests help towards sound design.

COMPUTATION PANELS NINE

Prerequisite reading: Chapters 2 to 8 inclusive

Reminders
Be familiar with all the reminders for Computation Panels Two to Eight inclusive.

CP9A
PROBLEM: To decide on an allowable bearing pressure from the results of a simple site investigation without examination of consolidation characteristics

Data
The investigation was carried out for a proposed county library on a steeply sloping site. The ground area covered by the building was small; only three boreholes were driven. Since it was expected to erect the building on strip footings, the borings were taken to a depth of 20 ft. only, sufficient for a narrow strip footing even if founded at some feet below the surface.

Undisturbed samples were extracted from the boreholes at the following depths:

Borehole A: 6, 9, 15 and 18 feet below ground level
Borehole B: 3, 6, 9, 12, 15 and 18 feet below ground level
Borehole C: as for B.

The levels of the three holes above datum at ground level were 18·7, 24·3 and 23·6 feet respectively for A, B and C.

Figure CP9A shows the most important data extracted. It is always advisable to draw out the logs of the boreholes in this way, for various points come to light. For example, the boulder clay lies at a level depth between B and C, and is somewhat lower at A. In fact, the boulder clay was found to slope at 1 : 8 from B to A, the surface slope being slightly less steep.

Other routine data such as moisture content and density were also recorded for all the samples. Samples below the top of the boulder clay were found to be purely cohesive and did not show an angle of

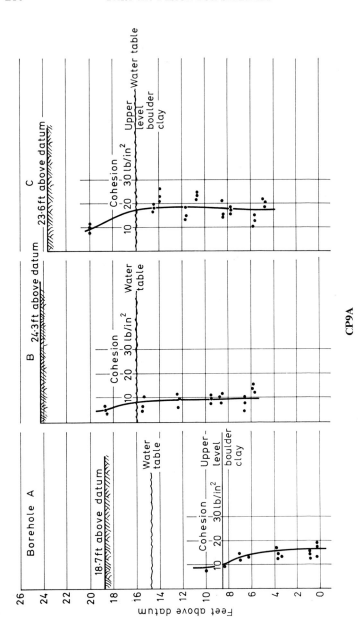

CP9A

shearing resistance on the immediate test. Most were, therefore, tested in unconfined compression. The results are given in Fig. CP9A. Above the boulder clay any clayey samples were also tested for cohesion (Table CP9A).

Table CP9A

Depth below surface (ft)	Borehole A			Borehole B			Borehole C		
	Moisture content m	γ (lb/ft³)	c (lb/in²)	m	γ (lb/ft³)	c (lb/in²)	m	γ (lb/ft³)	c (lb/in²)
3	—	—	—	0·20	112	—	0·21	103	—
6	0·20	119	—	0·26	126	—	0·19	139	—
9	0·27	122	—	0·16	121	13	0·15	142	21
12	—	—	—	0·16	140	14	0·15	139	20
15	0·16	136	14	0·16	134	10	0·15	138	18
18	0·16	141	14	0·16	140	10	0·16	128	18

Results required

(a) Advice on the levels at which footings for the library should be placed.

(b) Suggested value of allowable bearing pressure at the depths selected.

Method of attack

(1) From the boring logs, the jar samples and the undisturbed samples it is established that the material lying above the boulder clay is weak and variable. Footings placed in this material would almost certainly suffer differential settlement.

(2) The location of the boreholes allows at least of an estimate being made of the depth at which boulder clay will be found on the site. The surface of the boulder clay is nearly horizontal in one direction, and slopes at about 1 vertical to 8 horizontal in the other direction between A and B. If there is any flexibility about the location of the building, it is clear that, for the sake of economy, it should be located towards the top of this slope where the strong boulder clay is near the surface.

(3) Tests were carried out on the samples extracted and the

results are shown in Table CP9A. The lines across the table indicate where the overburden changes to boulder clay.

Some features are clearly indicated. The wet nature of the upper layers and their weaknesses in shear, as observed by inspection and by approximate checks, compare unfavourably with the stronger, heavier and drier boulder clay below. Figure CP9A shows how cohesion (angle of shearing resistance was zero for an immediate test) varies with depth.

(4) There is no homogeneity or reliable strength in the upper layers and a building such as that proposed must, by some means, be founded on the boulder clay.

(5) The next step is to determine the ultimate bearing capacity of the boulder clay. Since, for $\phi = 0$, $N_\gamma = 0$, only the first two terms of Terzaghi's equation need be used. In considering the location at borehole C, as an example of the procedure, we may accept 18 lb/in^2 for the value of cohesion. The ultimate bearing capacity is:

$$c = 18 \times 5 \cdot 7 \times 144 + 125 \times 7 \cdot 6 \times 1$$
$$= 14800 + 950 = 15750 \text{ lb/ft}^2$$
$$= 7 \text{ ton/ft}^2.$$

(6) The boulder clay is glacial in origin and is known to be overconsolidated. Likely values of $1/cm_v$ are then, say, from 75 to 150. If we assume a 2-inch settlement to be acceptable as a maximum, we have for the abscissa of Fig. 9.1 the values from 150 to 300. Reading off the value of the factor of safety for these, it is found to be the minimum of three, for a 5-ft wide strip footing, and somewhat above three for a 10-ft. wide footing and the lower values of $1/cm_v$.

(7) The allowable bearing pressure would thus be

$$= \frac{\text{Ultimate bearing capacity}}{3} + \text{relieving pressure of excavated soil}$$
$$= 7/3 + 7 \times 125/2240 = 2 \cdot 3 + 0 \cdot 4 = 2 \cdot 7 \text{ ton/ft}^2.$$

For wider footings than 5 ft, or with more stringent conditions about maximum settlement, the factor of safety applied to the ultimate bearing capacity must be increased.

(8) For a 10-ft wide footing and a requirement of about one inch of maximum settlement, the abscissae for Fig. 9.1 would be 75 to 150, giving factors of safety of from 9 to 5. If we assume 7 as a mean, the allowable bearing pressure would be 1·4 ton/ft^2.

CP9B

PROBLEM: To decide on an allowable bearing pressure for a raft foundation from a full site investigation

Data

The data given are for only one borehole out of a number driven to 60 ft during an extensive site investigation. At the location of this borehole it is intended to erect a heavy piece of industrial plant at a level which corresponds to 10 ft below the present ground level. The overburden will be removed for some distance around this site as large industrial plant is erected. It is likely that an area of about 20 ft square will be required as a minimum.

The data given on Fig. CP9B represent some of the information obtained at this particular borehole. It is always advisable to draw out graphs of the kind shown here, even if this has not been done in the site investigation report. A visual representation is of greater value than a table of figures. This material is clearly very uniform indeed. The coefficient of compressibility showed the same variation with pressure from samples taken at 10 ft and at 30 ft. The moisture content was uniform after the mixed surface layers were passed, and the bulk density was also very uniform at 125 lb/ft^3.

The material is a boulder clay, and some of the samples tested for cohesion had to be remoulded to eliminate stones. This material is known to have a sensitivity of unity—in other words, as for many remoulded clays, the structure has already been broken down and compressed, and further remoulding does not decrease the strength further. The samples were chiefly tested in unconfined compression. Only the first three were given a triaxial compression test, and when it was clear that the value of the angle of shearing resistance was zero, unconfined compression was used. Whether line A, B or C is chosen as depicting how the cohesion varies with depth, it is certain that there is no problem as would be presented by a weak layer. It would be prudent to assume that the shear strength of the clay for immediate loading is 20 lb/in^2 although something a little higher could be permitted if necessary.

Although the minimum area required was specified by the client, the load to be carried was not. Various types of plant were in question, some much heavier than others, but all weighing several hundred tons.

No more than three inches of settlement can be permitted relative to underground services serving the plant.

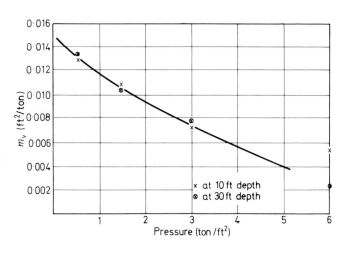

x at 10 ft depth
⊗ at 30 ft depth

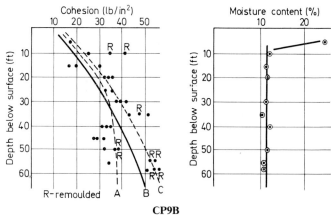

R-remoulded

CP9B

Results required

(a) What load can be carried safely on the minimum area. It is hoped that this area need not be exceeded.

(b) Advice on the design of the foundation so that differential settlement can be avoided.

Method of attack

(1) Since consolidation tests have been taken and the material shows quite distinct values of the coefficient of compressibility, a full estimation of the settlement of a 20 ft square raft is justified. A properly designed and rigid raft is clearly the only way in which heavy plant can be readily supported in these circumstances. This decision eliminates differential settlement and answers the second of the client's questions.

(2) Table CP9B/1 shows the usual derivation of the proportional stresses imposed at depths down to 50 feet. This allows of a mass of soil 40 ft deep to be investigated. This dimension is twice the width of the raft below the proposed founding level, and should enclose all the soil likely to be affected. Table 4C is used with a 10 ft square.

Table CP9B/1

z (ft)	B/z ($B = 10$ ft)	Influence factor (Table 4C)	Influence factor $\times 4$ (for 4 corners)
0	∞	0·250	1·00
5	2·0	0·232	0·93
10	1·0	0·175	0·70
20	0·5	0·084	0·34
25	0·4	0·060	0·24
50	0·2	0.018	0·07

The final column gives the proportion of the contact pressure (from the foundation) which is still acting as a vertical pressure at the depths indicated.

(3) Choosing 3, 2 and 1 ton/ft^2 at random, these figures are multiplied by the influence factors, the appropriate values of m_v selected from Fig. CP9B, and $m_v p$ calculated. The means of these latter values multiplied by the thickness of each layer (5·5, 10·5 and 25 ft) give the total likely settlement.

(4) From a quick sketch graph of pressure against settlement, the value of 1·7 ton/ft^2 is the maximum which can be permitted. The four inches of settlement which this will produce will occur over a long period. Without a calculation of the coefficient of consolidation, the rate at which this will take place is not known, but it may be

safely assumed that the first 50% must be guarded against in the early years of the life of the building.

(5) The load which can be carried is thus $1 \cdot 7 \times 400$ tons or 680 tons. If the plant and protecting building weigh less than this, the settlement will be less.

(6) A check on the factor of safety against shear failure should now be made, although it is unlikely that it is low. Since the overburden will be removed, the extra support given by the surcharge surrounding a deep footing will be eliminated, and, since there is no angle of shearing resistance, only the first term of the Terzaghi equation is required.

$$\text{Ultimate bearing capacity} = cN_c = 20 \times 144 \times 5 \cdot 7$$
$$= 16,420 \text{ lb/ft}^2$$
$$\text{or about } 7 \cdot 9 \text{ ton/ft}^2.$$

The factor of safety is thus $7 \cdot 9/1 \cdot 7 = 4 \cdot 5$ approximately. Another $0 \cdot 5$ ton/ft^2 can be added to this and to the figure in (8) to allow for overburden removed.

(7) A further check can be made by using Fig. 9.1 which gives a method of finding the approximate value of the factor of safety. Assuming a value of about 2 ton/ft^2 pressure, $m_v = 0 \cdot 009$ is obtained from Fig. CP9B. Multiplying this by the value of $c = 20$ lb/in^2 or $1 \cdot 3$ ton/ft^2 and finding the reciprocal gives about 86. Multiplying this by the four inches of maximum settlement gives 344. This is read off on the horizontal axis of Fig. 9.1 to give, for a 20-ft foundation, an approximate factor of safety of 4.

(8) This quick calculation gives an allowable bearing pressure of about 2 ton/ft^2 for a 4-inch settlement taking place over a long period. The figure checks well with the estimation from a settlement analysis, this time, but one is not always so fortunate. The problems in this chapter have, however, been taken from site investigations made in practice by the author and his colleagues. They show that there is some correspondence between the various methods, and that confidence can be built up by a knowledge of the behaviour of soil. Intuition and experience must still guide judgement. However "exact" these figures appear because they are written down in tables and shown in graphs, it must be remembered that there are many variables and many assumptions made. The result, however, gives the order of magnitude of the various quantities at least and allows

Table CP9B/2

Depth z (ft)	3 ton/ft² contact pressure					2 ton/ft² contact pressure					1 ton/ft² contact pressure				
	p Pressure at z (ton/ft²)	m_v (ft²/ton)	$m_v p$	Mean $m_v p$	Consolidation (ft)	p Pressure at z (ton/ft²)	m_v (ft²/ton)	$m_v p$	Mean $m_v p$	Consolidation (ft)	p Pressure at z (ton/ft²)	m_v (ft²/ton)	$m_v p$	Mean $m_v p$	Consolidation (ft)
0	3·00	0·007	0·024			2·00	0·009	0·018			1·00	0·012	0·012		
				0·023	0·12				0·017	0·09				0·012	0·06
5	2·78	0·008	0·022			1·86	0·009	0·017			0·93	0·012	0·012		
				0·021	0·10				0·016	0·08				0·012	0·05
10	2·10	0·009	0·019			1·40	0·011	0·015			0·70	0·012	0·008		
				0·016	0·16				0·012	0·12				0·010	0·06
20	1·01	0·012	0·012			0·67	0·013	0·008			0·34	0·013	0·004		
				0·010	0·05				0·007	0·04				0·006	0·02
25	0·72	0·012	0·008			0·48	0·013	0·006			0·24	0·014	0·003		
				0·006	0·14				0·004	0·10				0·004	0·05
50	0·20	0·014	0·003			0·14	0·014	0·002			0·07	0·014	0·001		
	Total settlement (ft) (in)				0·57 6·8					0·43 5·2				0·24 2·9

the architect to predict with confidence a range of properties within which the foundation substructures of his building must show conforming characteristics, if he has designed for safety.

Index